INTERNATIONAL BACCALAUREATE

STANDARD LEVEL CHEMISTRY

REVISION GUIDE AND WORKBOOK

FOR EXAMS BEGINNING MAY 2009

CAMERON LUMSDEN

FOR CLAIRE

1st Edition: July 2008

Acknowledgements

Thanks to Dr. Peter Morgan of Munich International School, and Martin Bluemel of Taunton school in Somerset for their gracious assistance in proofreading this text.

The purpose of this book

The purpose of this book is to highlight the types and styles of questions that are likely to appear on your IB Chemistry exam. There are Learning Check Questions designed to focus on a specific skill, and there are end of chapter questions that mimic the type of questions that IB Chemistry exams contain.

This book also highlights spots where students can often go wrong, where they get "trapped" by a tricky question, and how they should present their answers.

Who this book is for...

This book is intended for students who have already have been through the course material with a teacher and other resources. No text book can replace the ability of a teacher to guide student understanding.

How to use this book.

In many places in this text there is space for you to fill in information, but there is not a lot of blank space. You should keep a separate set of revision notes that are a hybrid of this book, your notes, your text etc.

Other resources

While studying it is important that you also have the following materials..

The Syllabus: You should use this as a check list, and understand what you know, and more importantly, what you don't know.

The Data Booklet: To date, the data booklet has not been used heavily by IBO during the exams, but you should be familiar with what is in it.

Past Papers: All teachers and IB Co-ordinators have access to past papers. Do as many as you can to get yourself familiar with the style and type of questions.

Your own course notes. - Hopefully you have maintained an accurate record of the material that you have covered in your classes. You should compare the way your teacher presents information, the way your textbook presents information, and the way information is presented here. They should all be effectively the same! - However, perhaps one makes more sense to you. Compare and learn!

How to study

The best way to study for retention of information is to put yourself on a repeating cycle.

During your course, you have to do the daily work that the teacher assigns, but if you can, you should also regularly...

- Review what you did yesterday (last class)
- Review what you did last week
- Review what you did last month.

A tall order, but very effective if you can find the time - really you should make time - it's well invested as it will save you trying to "re-learn" everything.

Exam Review Time

You no doubt have six exams that you need to study for, but probably not all of them have the same priority.

Whatever the subject, you are best trying to learn slowly and regularly. If you have purchased this book in the Spring before your exams, you should make a plan to work on each unit of the course. You will probably need at least a week for each topic to...

- make notes
- learn definitions
- make flash cards (great if you take a bus to school)
- practice specific problem types
- do past paper questions

A warning! Cramming doesn't work. You either are not effective in learning material, you learn it superficially, or you run out of time to generate real understanding.

Slow and steady wins the race!

The Exams you face...

Paper 1 - 0:45 hour: 30 Multiple Choice questions (4 choices). No penalty for guessing.
NO CALCULATOR, NO DATABOOK

Paper 2 - 1:15 hours: Part A - Data based questions & short answer 40 points.
Part B - Extended response - choice of 1 of 3 questions 25 points each.
Calculator and Databook allowed.

Paper 1 & 2 are written "back to back" on the afternoon of the given day. Meaning that you will be in the exam room for a possible 2:00 hours - by the time you get seated etc. Get comfortable!

Paper 2 & 3 are allowed 5 minutes reading time. Use this time in Paper 2 to start considering the choice of which questions you will answer - Don't waste time pre-reading Part A - you have to do it anyway!

Paper 3 - 1:00 hours: You answer questions on the two option topics that you have studied.
Short answer only

Your Grade

Paper 1   20%   Note: The "Core" of the course - Paper 1&2
Paper 2   36%   count for 52% of you final grade.
Paper 3   20%
Lab Reports   24%

Typical Overall SL Grade Boundaries

These vary from year to year but the following table gives you a rough idea.
Grades are calculated based on your RAW score, not the 1-7 scale - 39/40 is better than 38/40 even though they are both "7" - The "7" is for guidance only.

1	2	3	4	5	6	7
0–19%	20% – 34%	35% – 47%	48% – 59%	60% – 69%	70 – 79%	80 – 100%

Atomic Number
Symbol
Relative mass

1	2	3	4	5	6	7	8	9	10	11	12	13	14	15	16	17	18
1 **H** 1.01																	2 **He** 4.00
3 **Li** 6.94	4 **Be** 9.01											5 **B** 10.81	6 **C** 12.01	7 **N** 14.01	8 **O** 16.00	9 **F** 19.00	10 **Ne** 20.18
11 **Na** 22.99	12 **Mg** 24.31											13 **Al** 26.98	14 **Si** 28.09	15 **P** 30.97	16 **S** 32.06	17 **Cl** 35.45	18 **Ar** 39.95
19 **K** 39.10	20 **Ca** 40.08	21 **Sc** 44.96	22 **Ti** 47.90	23 **V** 50.94	24 **Cr** 52.00	25 **Mn** 54.94	26 **Fe** 55.85	27 **Co** 58.93	28 **Ni** 58.71	29 **Cu** 63.55	30 **Zn** 65.37	31 **Ga** 69.72	32 **Ge** 72.59	33 **As** 74.92	34 **Se** 78.96	35 **Br** 79.90	36 **Kr** 83.80
37 **Rb** 85.47	38 **Sr** 87.62	39 **Y** 88.91	40 **Zr** 91.22	41 **Nb** 92.91	42 **Mo** 95.94	43 **Tc** 98.91	44 **Ru** 101.07	45 **Rh** 102.91	46 **Pd** 106.42	47 **Ag** 107.87	48 **Cd** 112.40	49 **In** 114.82	50 **Sn** 118.69	51 **Sb** 121.75	52 **Te** 127.60	53 **I** 126.90	54 **Xe** 131.30
55 **Cs** 132.91	56 **Ba** 137.34	57 **La** 138.91	72 **Hf** 178.49	73 **Ta** 180.95	74 **W** 183.85	75 **Re** 186.21	76 **Os** 190.21	77 **Ir** 192.22	78 **Pt** 195.09	79 **Au** 196.97	80 **Hg** 200.59	81 **Tl** 204.37	82 **Pb** 207.19	83 **Bi** 208.98	84 **Po** (210)	85 **At** (210)	86 **Rn** (222)
87 **Fr** (223)	88 **Ra** (226)																

TABLE OF CONTENTS

CHAPTER 1

QUANTITATIVE CHEMISTRY

Introduction

Jeremias Benjaim Richter (1762-1807) was the first to lay down the principles of stoichiometry. In 1792 he wrote:

"Die Stöchyometrie (Stöchyometria) ist die Wissenschaft die Quantitativen oder Massenverhältnisse zu messen, in welchen die chymischen Elemente gegen einander stehen."

"Stoichiometry is the science of measuring the quantitative proportions or mass ratios in which chemical elements stand to one another."

Or more simply put, everything in this unit is a simple ratio. As long as you know one quantity, you can figure out the others by applying a ratio.

Exam Hint

Be clear and organized. You may have many numbers floating around on your page. It's very helpful if, after solving a step in a problem, you write " $n=5.5$ mol $\underline{of\ H_2}$", or $n(H_2)=5.5$ mol not just "*5.5*" ALWAYS INCLUDE THE UNITS and the species, TO REMIND YOURSELF OF WHAT YOU HAVE SOLVED FOR.

Throughout this unit (and all others), you should be obeying the rules of significant figures. Significant Figures are covered in Chapter 11.

Special Note on Sig Figs.

Worked examples in this chapters show intermediate answers which are rounded to the appropriate number of significant figures, However, the calculator answer is retained for further steps.

Mole Concept

Chemists work on a particle basis – one particle of this reacts with three particles of that to produce two particles of product. It doesn't matter at the moment what those particles actually are – they could be atoms, diatomic molecules, larger molecules, ions, electrons, etc. The problem is that it takes an awful lot of particles to get an amount that can be manipulated on the "human scale" – as opposed to the "atomic scale".

So knowing what the atomic masses were in terms of protons, neutrons (and electrons), it was decided that we would use the same value of atomic mass and scale it up to the "gram-equivalent mass". As long as all elements were scaled up the same amount, the relative mass would be the same.

It turns out that the scale factor is rather large (because atoms are rather small!) – it is 6.02×10^{23}.

Definition

> *One mole contains the same number of particles as 12.000 g of ^{12}C.*
> *12.000 g of ^{12}C contains 6.02×10^{23} atoms.*

Now, you have to be careful of what types of particles you are talking about.

Example

1.0 mol of H_2O contains...

6.02×10^{23} **molecules** of water	
6.02×10^{23} oxygen **atoms**	the same number of oxygen atoms
1.2×10^{24} **atoms** of hydrogen	double the number of hydrogen atoms
1.8×10^{24} total **atoms**	triple the number of total atoms

Units

Just to put moles into perspective - moles can be treated the same as any other unit. Moles measure the "amount of substance", which fundamentally means the **number** of particles - not the qualities of those particles, like mass or volume.

Quantity	Unit	Symbol	Example
Mass	gram	g	m= 5.0 g
Length	meter	m	l= 0.025 m
Time	second	s	t= 35.5 s
Temperature	Kelvin	K	T= 298 K
	Degrees Celsius	°C	T= 25.2°C
Amount of Substance	Mole	mol	n= 3.5×10^{-2} mol

Table 1.1: SI Units

Note: We use "n" for <u>n</u>umber of moles.

Mole – Particle Conversions

There are lots of different ways to remember this… The easiest is to remember the idea- it takes 6.02×10^{23} particles to make 1.0 mol.

Number of Particles = number of moles x 6.02×10^{23}

Expression

Remember: it doesn't matter what mass the particles have – you are just converting the number – it's like converting single eggs to dozens of eggs and vice versa – this is easy, because the value for "dozen" is always 12.

Determine the number of particles in the following amounts.
a) 2.0 mol of neon
b) 0.125 mol of zoopers
c) 1.5 mol of widgets
d) 1.25×10^{-3} mol of ions
e) 12.5 μmol of electrons*
f) 4.55×10^{-9} mol of particles
g) 5.3 mol of gold atoms
h) 1.85×10^{-2} mol of things
*$\mu = 10^{-6}$

1.1 Learning Check

Determine the number of moles in the following amounts.
a) 6.02×10^{25}
b) 2.26×10^{23}
c) 3.31×10^{24}
d) 7.53×10^{20}
e) 3.46×10^{18}
f) 5.27×10^{19}
g) 2.56×10^{20}
h) 1.05×10^{24}

1.2 Learning Check

Molar Mass

Molar mass is the mass of one mole of a substance, and is the "gram-equivalent mass" of the relative atomic mass on the periodic table.

Definition

The easiest way to think about this is that the mass numbers on the periodic table can be thought of as follows…

1 atom of oxygen = 16 atomic mass units (8 p + 8 n)
6.02×10^{23} atoms of oxygen = 16.00 g of oxygen atoms
1 mol of oxygen atoms = 16.00 g of oxygen atoms

Notice the last two are the same!

The numbers on the periodic table are for ONE MOLE or ONE ATOM, so everything is just a multiple of it.

$$Al_2(SO_4)_3 = \begin{array}{lll} 2 \times Al & = & 2 \times 26.98 \text{ g mol}^{-1} & = 53.96 \text{ g mol}^{-1} \\ + \quad 3 \times S & = & 3 \times 32.06 \text{ g mol}^{-1} & = 96.18 \text{ g mol}^{-1} \\ + \quad 12 \times O & = & 12 \times 16.00 \text{ g mol}^{-1} & = 192.00 \text{ g mol}^{-1} \\ \hline Al_2(SO_4)_3 & & & = 342.14 \text{ g mol}^{-1} \end{array}$$

HINT: Your calculator knows the order of operations, try doing it all on one line!

1.3 Learning Check

Calculate the molar mass of the following formulas. (To two decimal places)
a) $NaCl$
b) Na_2CO_3
c) NH_4NO_3
d) $CaCl_2$
e) $Ca_3(PO_4)_2$
f) $MgSO_4 \cdot 7H_2O$
g) Fe_2O_3
h) $(NH_4)_3PO_4$
i) CH_3COOH

NOTE: in (f) the compound is a hydrate, and contains 7 moles of water for each mole of ionic salt

Mole – Mass Conversions

To find the mass of a given number of moles, we simply need to multiply by how many moles we have, and we know the mass of one mole from the periodic table.

Expression

$$\boxed{\text{mass} = \text{number of moles} \times \text{molar mass}}$$

in terms of units…

$$\boxed{\text{grams} = \text{moles} \times \frac{\text{grams}}{\text{mole}}}$$

Expression

1.4 Learning Check

Calculate the mass of the following.
a) 1.50 mol of $LiCl$
b) 2.25 mol of $Ca(OH)_2$
c) 0.165 mol of $CuCl_2$
d) 7.50×10^{-6} mol of Al_2O_3
e) 5.00×10^{-3} mol of Na_2CO_3
f) 8.75×10^{-9} mol of PbI_2
g) 0.750 mol of $MgSO_4$
h) 3.75×10^{-6} mol of $AgNO_3$
i) 2.500 mol of H_2SO_4

1.5 Learning Check

Calculate the amount (number of moles) of the following.
a) 10.0 g of $CuSO_4$
b) 10.0 g of $MgSO_4$
c) 10.0 g of Na_2SO_4
d) 0.550 g of $NaOH$
e) 6.25 g of $BaCl_2$
f) 55.8 g of ZnO
g) 25.75 g of $SnCl_4$
h) 5.05 g of $HgCl_2$
i) 1.00 g of $Na_2B_4O_7$

Balancing Equations

A chemical reaction can never create or destroy matter (atoms); it can only rearrange them. Therefore, we must have the same number of atoms of each type on each side of the equation.

Balancing equations means that you multiply each (correct) formula by a coefficient so that you obtain equal numbers of each type of atom on each side of the equation.

Some people say there are rules for balancing equations, but they are more like guidelines. The best guideline is...

Leave uncombined elements until the end – e.g. $O_2(g)$, $H_2(g)$, $K(s)$, etc., because when you change their coefficient, you don't mess up anything else!

Tip

At the moment, we don't want any fractions – so you may have double all coefficients in order to clear the fraction.

Later we might need to use fractions because our equation must obey a definition (usually in order to produce only one mole of product) – See Energetics - Heat of Combustion and Heat of Formation.

Balance the following equations.

1.6 Learning Check

a) $\_\_K + \_\_H_2O \rightarrow \_\_H_2 + \_\_KOH$

b) $\_\_CuO + \_\_NH_3 \rightarrow \_\_H_2O + \_\_N_2 + \_\_Cu$

c) $\_\_Al + \_\_HCl \rightarrow \_\_AlCl_3 + \_\_H_2$

d) $\_\_ZnS + \_\_O_2 \rightarrow \_\_ZnO + \_\_SO_2$

e) $\_\_NH_4Cl + \_\_Ca(OH)_2 \rightarrow \_\_CaCl_2 + \_\_NH_3 + \_\_H_2O$

f) $\_\_C_4H_{10} + \_\_O_2 \rightarrow \_\_CO_2 + \_\_H_2O$

g) $\_\_H_3PO_4 + \_\_NaOH \rightarrow \_\_Na_3PO_4 + \_\_H_2O$

h) $\_\_C_2H_2 + \_\_O_2 \rightarrow \_\_CO_2 + \_\_H_2O$

i) $\_\_KClO_3 \rightarrow \_\_KCl + \_\_O_2$

j) $\_\_C_2H_6 + \_\_O_2 \rightarrow \_\_CO_2 + \_\_H_2O$

k) $\_\_N_2 + \_\_H_2 \rightarrow \_\_NH_3$

l) $\_\_N_2H_4 + \_\_O_2 \rightarrow \_\_N_2 + \_\_H_2O$

m) $\_\_Na + \_\_Cl_2 \rightarrow \_\_NaCl$

n) $\_\_Fe + \_\_O_2 \rightarrow \_\_Fe_2O_3$

Mole Relationships in a Chemical Reaction

A chemical reaction shows you the relative number of moles of all species in a chemical reaction. It's like a recipe.

2 parts hydrogen plus one part oxygen makes two parts water. – It's just that our "parts" are moles.

$$2H_2(g) + O_2(g) \rightarrow 2H_2O$$

$$\frac{H_2}{O_2} = \frac{2}{1}$$

The coefficients in the balanced reaction give us the mole ratio of any two species, so, if you know the number H_2, you can solve for O_2.

Example   *How many moles of O_2 are required to react with 6.284 mol of H_2?*

$$\frac{H_2}{O_2} = \frac{2}{1} = \frac{6.284 \text{ mol}}{x}$$

$$2x = 6.284 \text{ mol}$$

$$x = 3.142 \text{ mol of } O_2$$

It doesn't matter which two species you are concerned with, you always know one of them and the ratio will give you other one.

Example   *How many moles of each product are produced from 32 mol of nitric acid?*

$$3Cu(s) + 8HNO_3(aq) \rightarrow 3Cu(NO_3)_2(aq) + 2NO(g) + 4H_2O(l)$$

$\dfrac{HNO_3}{Cu(NO_3)_2} = \dfrac{8}{3} = \dfrac{32}{x}$	$\dfrac{NO}{HNO_3} = \dfrac{2}{8} = \dfrac{x}{32}$	$\dfrac{HNO_3}{H_2O} = \dfrac{8}{4} = \dfrac{32}{x}$
$8x = 3 \times 32$ mol of $Cu(NO_3)_2$	$8x = 2 \times 32$ mol of NO	$8x = 4 \times 32$ mol of H_2O
$x = 12$ mol of $Cu(NO_3)_2$	$x = 8$ mol of NO	$x = 16$ mol of H_2O

Note: Notice that it doesn't matter which is on the top of the fraction – you are going to cross multiply anyway.

YOU DO NEED TO KEEP THINGS LINED UP THOUGH! - In the example, HNO_3 is always lined up with 8 and 32.

1.7 Learning Check

1. *Ammonia, NH_3, in produced by the Haber Process as follows*

$$N_2(g) + 3H_2(g) \rightleftharpoons 2NH_3(g)$$

How many moles of the following are required to make 5.0 mol of ammonia?
   a) *nitrogen*   b) *hydrogen*

2. *Propane, C_3H_8 burns in oxygen according to…*

$$C_3H_8 + 5O_2 \rightarrow 3CO_2 + 4H_2O$$

   a) *How many moles of oxygen are required to react with…*
      i)   *3.0 mol of propane?*
      ii) *20.0 mol of propane?*
      iii) *0.50 mol of propane?*
   b) *If 50.0 mol of oxygen are available, what is the maximum number of moles of propane that can be burned?*
   c) *How many moles of water are produced in each question in a)?*

3. The combustion of octane, a major component in petrol is represented by the following…

$$2C_8H_{18} + 25O_2(g) \rightarrow 16CO_2(g) + 18 H_2O(g)$$

   a) How many moles of oxygen are required to react with 5.00 mol of octane?

   b) How many moles of octane must be burned to produce 7.2 mol of water?

   c) i) If 2.20 mol of carbon dioxide were produced from the reaction, how many moles of water are produced at the same time?

      ii) How many moles of octane must have been burned?

Mass Relationships in a Chemical Reaction

Simple stoichiometry questions always follow the same three steps, and you have done them already, you just combine a mass - mole conversion and then apply the ratio from the balanced equation.

A special note about molar masses…
The molar mass is always for ONE mole. **Do not apply the coefficient to the molar mass.** That would mean that the molar mass of hydrogen depends on what it was reacting with - it doesn't.
The ratio of coefficients is used to convert from moles of one species into moles of another species.

Common Mistake

Consider the reaction of 24 g of hydrogen in both of the following reactions

$$2H_2(g) + O_2(g) \rightarrow 2H_2O(g)$$

$$3H_2(g) + N_2(g) \rightarrow 2NH_3(g)$$

WRONG – It's wrong to say that you have 24 g $\div$ 4 g•mol^{-1} = 6 mol in the water reaction and 24 g $\div$ 6 g•mol^{-1} = 4 mol of hydrogen in the ammonia reaction. The moles of hydrogen you have are independent of the reaction it is undergoing.

CORRECT - Because you have the same number of grams in both, you have the same number of moles in both – i.e. 24 g$\div$2 g•mol^{-1} = 12 moles of hydrogen.
The ratio of the moles of hydrogen to oxygen or nitrogen is 2:1 or 3:1 respectively and is used to find out information about the other species in the reaction, in this case, nitrogen or oxygen or the products.

> 1. Divide by the molar mass of what you have in grams (to get moles).
>
> 2. Convert moles of X to moles of Y by applying the ratio from the balanced equation.
>
> 3. Multiply by the molar mass of Y to obtain the mass of Y.
>
>   It's simple: Divide, Ratio, Multiply.

Problem solving steps

1.8 Learning Check

1. *Ethanol can be used as a supplement in petrol to make "gasohol". Ethanol burns according to ...*

$$C_2H_5OH + 3O_2 \rightarrow 2CO_2(g) + 3H_2O(g)$$

   a) *What mass of oxygen is required to react with 1200 g of ethanol?*
   b) *If 655 g of water is produced, what mass of ethanol was burned?*

2. *One of the steps involved in obtaining a metal from its sulphide is "roasting". Iron sulphide is an example..*

$$4FeS(s) + 7O_2(g) \rightarrow 2Fe_2O_3(s) + 4SO_2(g)$$

   What mass of iron (III) oxide can be obtained by the roasting of 774g of the sulphide?

3. *Silver is used for jewellery and tableware. It becomes tarnished when exposed to small quantities of H_2S.*

$$4Ag(s) + 2H_2S(g) + O_2(g) \rightarrow 2Ag_2S(s) + 2H_2O(g)$$

   What mass of silver sulphide would form from the reaction of 0.015 g of silver?

4. *The Ostwald process is how nitric acid is formed. The first step is the reaction of ammonia and oxygen in the presence of a catalyst. The equation is...*

$$4NH_3(g) + 5O_2(g) \xrightarrow{catalyst} 4NO_2(g) + 6H_2O(g)$$

   a) *What mass of oxygen is required to completely react with 1.22 kg of ammonia?*
   b) *What mass of $NO_2(g)$ is produced at the same time?*

5. *The metal tungsten, which is used in light bulbs can be obtained by heating its oxide with hydrogen*

$$WO_3(s) + 3H_2(g) \rightarrow W(s) + 3H_2O(g)$$

   a) *What mass of tungsten can be obtained from 250.0 g of tungsten(VI) oxide?*
   b) *What mass of hydrogen is required for part a)?*

Limiting Reactant

The dreaded question, but also a popular one with IB Examiners because they can get more concepts covered for less candidate time.

As far as you are concerned, it's the same as the previous question, but now you have been given two (or more) reactants and you need to decide which one (there is always only one) will give you the correct amount of product.

Problem solving steps

1. Determine the number of moles of **each** reactant

2. Determine the limiting reactant – this is the new step

3. Use the limiting reactant to find the moles of the product (just like before)

4. Calculate the mass of the product. – just like before.

So how do we do the new step?

There are lots of ways, but remember the limiting reactant is determined to be the reactant which has the fewest number of moles *in terms of the molar ratio of reactants*. (It's the last bit that lots of students forget)

The easiest way to compare the number of moles of each reactant with respect to the molar ratio required is to do a quick check by forcing the ratio to be against 1. In order to do this, divide the moles of each reactant by its coefficient in the balanced equation.

THIS IS A CHECK ONLY – YOU DO NOT USE THIS NUMBER FOR ANY CALCULATIONS.

What amount of ammonia can be produced by the reaction of 100.0 g of   Example
N_2(g) and 15.0 g of H_2(g)?

$$N_2(g) + 3H_2(g) \rightleftharpoons 2NH_3(g)$$

$$n_{N_2} = \frac{100.0\ g}{28.02\ g\ mol^{-1}} = 3.568879372 = 3.569\ mol\ (4\ s.f.$$

$$n_{H_2} = \frac{15.0\ g}{2.02\ g\ mol^{-1}} = 7.425742574 = 7.43\ mol\ (3\ s.f.)$$

Now we know the moles of each reactant, but we need to find the lesser with respect to the ratio in the balanced equation so we do the following quick check.   The New Step

$$\frac{7.43\ mol\ of\ H_2}{3} = 2.48 \qquad\qquad \frac{3.569\ mol\ of\ N_2}{1} = 3.569$$

Because the value for H_2 is the lesser, this is our limiting reactant, and N_2 is "in excess" (INXS).

Alternately, we can see that we require three times as much hydrogen as nitrogen - do we have it? - NO, the amount of hydrogen is less than what we need, therefore it is the limiting reactant.

Now we use the limiting reactant for everything, and all other amounts are relative to it.

To answer the question finally...   Continue as
                                                                                                                                     before

$$\frac{product}{limiting\ reactant} = \frac{NH_3}{H_2} = \frac{2}{3} = \frac{x}{7.43\ mol}$$

$$3x = 2 \times 7.43\ mol$$

$$x = 4.95\ mol\ of\ NH_3$$

It doesn't matter which way you have the fraction as long as all species are lined up.

Now, finish the problem by find the mass of 4.95 moles of ammonia.

$$mass = number\ of\ moles \times molar\ mass$$

$$m = n \times M_r$$

$$m = 4.95\ mol \times 17.04\ g\ mol^{-1}$$

$$m = 84.4\ g\ of\ NH_3\ \ (3\ s.f.)$$

1.9 Learning
Check

1. *Ethane burns in oxygen as follows*

$$2C_2H_6(g) + 7O_2(g) \rightarrow 4CO_2(g) + 6H_2O(g)$$

If 10.2 g of ethane and 44.6 g of oxygen are mixed and ignited...
a) *determine the moles of ethane and oxygen.*
b) *determine the limiting reactant.*
c) *determine the mass of carbon dioxide produced.*

2. *Sodium phosphate can be prepared by the following...*

$$3NaOH + H_3PO_4 \rightarrow Na_3PO_4 + 3H_2O$$

If 36.0 g of NaOH is reacted with 12.0 g of H_3PO_4...
a) *Determine the limiting reactant.*
b) *What mass of sodium phosphate should be produced?*

3. *100.0 g of each oxygen and butane(C_4H_{10}), are combusted.*
a) *Write the balanced equation for the combustion reaction.*
b) *Identify the amount of each reactant in moles.*
c) *Identify the limiting reactant.*
d) *Identify the masses of both products formed.*

Solutions

A solution contains a solute dissolved in a solvent, and the molar concentration is expressed as moles of solute per cubic decimetre of solution (not solvent).
A solution is made by dissolving the required amount of solute in a minimum of solvent, and then adding what ever amount of solvent is required to reach the desired volume.
The molar concentration is called molarity. It may be written in two different ways. The fundamental units "mol dm^{-3}" or simply "M". (Which is often underlined or bold)
e.g.   The student was using a 0.25 mol•dm^{-3} solution = 0.25 M solution.

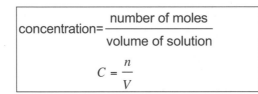

$$concentration = \frac{number\ of\ moles}{volume\ of\ solution}$$

$$C = \frac{n}{V}$$

where C is the concentration in mol dm^{-3}, n is the number of moles, and V is the volume in dm^3.
IB and most other organisations are moving towards using dm^3 as the basic unit of volume. However the term "liter" is still popular in language and texts. One liter is defined as 1 dm^3.

1 dm^3 = 1.0 L =1000 mL = 1000 cm^3

Making solutions and determining solute mass.

You need to be able to state how to make a certain volume and concentration of solution.

What mass of $NaHCO_3$ is required to make 250 cm³ of a 0.350 M solution?

Solution:

$n=CV$

$n=0.350$ mol dm⁻³ $\times 0.250$ dm³

$n = 0.0875$ mol of $NaHCO_3$ required

$mass = n \times M_r$

$mass = 0.0875$ mol $\times 84.01$ g mol⁻¹

$mass = 7.35$ g $NaHCO_3(s)$ required

Mix 7.35 g of $NaHCO_3(s)$ in some water and add water up to 250 cm³.

Example

Determine the concentration of the following solutions.
a) 250 cm³ containing 45.0 g of $MgSO_4$
b) 0.100 dm³ containing 10.0 g of NaCl
c) 500 cm³ containing 2.42 g of $Fe(NO_3)_3$
d) 25.0 cm³ containing 0.210 g of $NaHCO_3$

1.10 Learning Check

Determine the mass of solute required to make the following solutions.
e) 1.00 dm³ of 0.25 M KI
f) 250.0 cm³ of 0.1 M $AgNO_3$
g) 100.0 cm³ of 0.25 M NaOH
h) 0.500 dm³ of 0.40 M $Mg(NO_3)_2$

Kinetic Molecular Theory

The Kinetic Molecular Theory states that …

1)   Particles are in constant motion and…
2)   That motion depends upon the *absolute* temperature

Simply put, absolute zero means there is virtually no particle motion – all translational, rotational and vibrational motion stops. So you can't go below absolute zero, because once motion is stopped, it can't be more stopped!!

Temperature is therefore a measure of kinetic energy or motion of particles. Greater temperature means that the particles have greater kinetic energy. The absolute temperature scale is measured in Kelvin. Zero Kelvin means zero kinetic energy.

Pressure

Pressure - the force per unit area that the particles exert through collisions with the container walls.

Definition

Pressure can be measured in many different ways, all of which have some historical basis. However, the two common pressure units in IB Chemistry are kilopascals (kPa) and atmospheres (atm).

1 atm = 101.325 kPa

Boyle's Law

Boyle's Law is the relationship between volume and pressure. Pressure and volume are inversely proportional. As the volume decreases, the particles are forced closer together and so, the number of collisions with the sides of the container increases, and thus pressure increases.

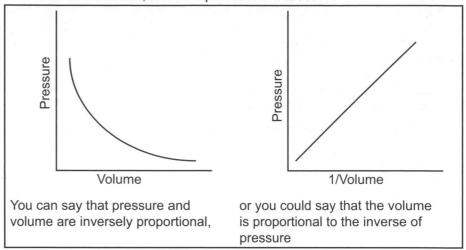

You can say that pressure and volume are inversely proportional,

or you could say that the volume is proportional to the inverse of pressure

Figure 1.2: Pressure and Volume graphical relationships.

$$Pressure \propto \frac{1}{Volume}$$

$$P \propto \frac{1}{V}$$

$$PV = constant$$

$$(PV)_{condition\ 1} = constant = (PV)_{condition\ 2}$$

Expression

$$\boxed{P_1V_1 = P_2V_2}$$

Pressure Law

This is the relationship between pressure and temperature.
As temperature increases, the kinetic energy of the particles increases, therefore they are colliding with the sides of the container with greater frequency **and** force. Both of these factors cause the pressure to increase.

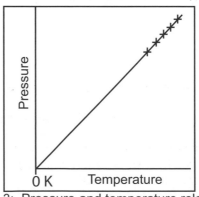

Figure 1.3: Pressure and temperature relationship

If the particles have zero kinetic energy at zero Kelvin, then they can't collide with the container walls.

Charles' Law

Charles' Law is the relationship between volume and temperature
As temperature increases, so does the kinetic energy of the particles. This causes them to collide more frequently and with more force, and therefore spread out.

$$Volume \propto Temperature$$

$$V \propto T$$

$$\frac{V}{T} = constant$$

$$(\frac{V}{T})_{condition\ 1} = constant = (\frac{V}{T})_{condition\ 2}$$

$$\boxed{\frac{V_1}{T_1} = \frac{V_2}{T_2}}$$

Expression

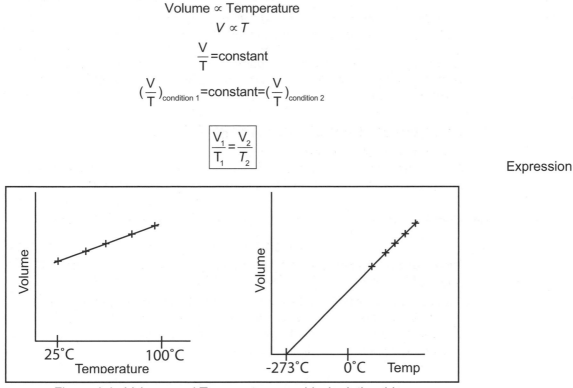

Figure 1.4: Volume and Temperature graphical relationships

Generally, volume is proportional to temperature, however, zero volume can only exist at zero KELVIN, not zero Celsius. - see Ideal Gases.
Watch out for changes involving a doubling or tripling of Celsius degrees, the proportionality only works for the absolute (Kelvin) scale.

Exam Trap

The Combined Gas Law

If we put Boyle's, Charles' and the pressure law together we get,

$$\boxed{\frac{P_1V_1}{T_1} = \frac{P_2V_2}{T_2}}$$

How will the volume of an ideal gas change when the pressure is quadrupled and the absolute temperature is tripled?

Example

$$\frac{P_1V_1}{T_1} = \frac{(4P_1)V_2}{(3T_1)}$$

$$\frac{P_1V_1(3T_1)}{(4P_1)T_1} = V_2$$

$$\frac{3}{4}V_1 = V_2$$

The new volume, V_2 will be $^3/_4$ of the original volume, V_1.

Avogadro's Law

Up until now, we have been concerned only with a fixed amount (or mass) of gas. Now we consider how changing the number of moles (amount) of gas affects its volume. Avogadro's Law is the relationship between number of particles and volume.

Definition

> *Avogadro's Law states that equal volumes of gas (at equal pressure and temperature) must contain an equal number of moles of gas.*

Or put another way, volume is proportional to the number of moles at constant pressure, or pressure is proportional to the number of moles at constant volume

Avogadro's Law of Combining Volumes

A popular type of multiple-choice question on Paper 1.
Avogadro's Law simply means that you can treat moles and volume or moles and pressure as proportional if all other factors remain constant.

Classic Question   *Consider the Haber Process for the production of ammonia.*

$$N_2(g) + 3H_2(g) \rightleftharpoons 2NH_3(g)$$

What volume of ammonia will be produced by the reaction of 4 dm³ of N_2 and 9 dm³ of H_2?

Consider this as a limiting reactant question. The molar ratio of N_2 to H_2 is 1:3. Is 9 dm³ three times greater than 4 dm³? - NO! We need 12 dm³ of H_2. We only have 9, so H_2 is the limiting reactant, and we always use the limiting reactant to figure out the amount of product.

$$\frac{H_2}{NH_3} = \frac{3}{2} = \frac{9}{x}$$

$$3x = 18$$

$$x = 6$$

$$NH_3 = 6 \text{ dm}^3$$

Standard Molar Volume

Standard molar volume is the volume of one mole of any gas at standard temperature and pressure for a gas - 1 atm and 273 K (0°C).

Definition

> *1.0 mol of any gas occupies 22.4 dm³ @ Standard Conditions (STP)*

Do not confuse with the value for RTP - "room" temperature and pressure, which (thankfully) is 25°C, not 0°C, so the volume is bigger - 24.0 dm³. - and the value of 24 dm³ is easier to do mental math with.

Whenever you have been given information about gases, check to see if they are at Standard conditions (1 atm & 273K) - If it is, then you don't need to use $PV=nRT$, you can simply use $V=22.4$ dm³mol⁻¹! This value is given in the data booklet.

A sample of 0.0412 g of a gas has a volume of 35.4 cm³ at 1 atm and 273K, what is the molar mass of the gas?

Example

$$n = \frac{0.0354 \text{ dm}^3}{22.4 \text{ dm}^3\text{mol}^{-1}}$$

$$n = 0.00158 \text{ mol}$$

$$M_r = \frac{0.0412 \text{ g}}{0.00158 \text{ mol}}$$

$$M_r = 26.1 \text{ g mol}^{-1}$$

Ideal Gas Law

*An ideal gas is a gas that does **not** have any...*

Definition

1. molecular volume nor any
    - so that the volume of a gas can go to zero
    - (ignore volume of particles)

2. intermolecular forces
    - so that the gas never condenses to a liquid
    - (ignore intermolecular forces of attraction)

Most gases behave as Ideal Gases because the volume of the gas is usually so much bigger than the volume of the actual molecules that it is negligible, and they are at temperatures far above the boiling/condensation points that the IMFs are insignificant.

Gases exhibit "non-ideal" behaviour when they are under high pressures, and low temperatures.

Ideal Gas Law Relationship is

$$PV = nRT$$

You must make sure that you pay attention to units.

Exam Trap

Most students learn that the value for R; the ideal gas constant is 8.314, but many forget that the units of $kPa \cdot dm^3 \cdot mol^{-1} \cdot K^{-1}$. There are other values of R that relate to other units of pressure and volume. Becareful, the units in the databook are given as $J \text{ mol}^{-1}K^{-1}$, which is the same as $kPa \cdot dm^3 \cdot mol^{-1} \cdot K^{-1}$.

The most common mistake is to not pay attention to the units in the question. Lots of times, exams give information in similar units like Pa not kPa, and if you don't convert your answer is off by a factor of 1000, which can lead to some strange answers.

Common Mistake

Calculate the molar mass of a volatile liquid / gas.

Classic Question

You are given the mass of a gas, the volume and conditions, and must find the molar mass. As molar mass is only the mass per mole, you have all the information you need. Mass is given and you can rearrange PV=nRT to find number of moles, n.

Example

An unknown gas of mass 0.625 g occupies a volume of 35.1 cm³ at 25˚C and 1x10⁵ Pa. Calculate the molar mass of the gas.

Don't forget to convert quantities to the correct units!!!	$PV = nRT$ $n = \dfrac{PV}{RT}$
25˚C = 298K 1.00x10⁵ Pa = 100 kPa 35.1cm³ = 0.351 dm³	$n = \dfrac{(100 \text{ kPa}) \times (0.351 \text{ dm}^3)}{(8.314 \text{ kPa} \cdot \text{dm}^3 \cdot \text{mol}^{-1} \cdot \text{K}^{-1}) \times (298 \text{ K})}$ $n = 0.0142 \text{ mol}$
	$\text{molar mass} = \dfrac{\text{mass}}{\text{moles}} = \dfrac{0.625 \text{ g}}{0.0142 \text{ mol}} = 44.12 \text{ g} \cdot \text{mol}^{-1}$

Remember to use common sense - the molar mass of any volatile gas is likely going to be between 20 and 200 g•mol⁻¹.

Yield – Theoretical, Experimental and Percentage

The theoretical yield is simply the answer to a stoichiometry question – it's how much product you are supposed to get at the end of your experiment The experimental yield is what you actually do get. In most cases the experimental yield is less than the theoretical yield, but not always.

Reasons for low yield	Reasons for high yield
loss during transfer	insufficient drying
equilibrium / reaction did not go to completion	gain of oxygen (oxidation)
side reactions	side reactions

Definition

Percentage yield is the ratio of experimental to theoretical expressed as a percent.

$$\text{Percent Yield} = \frac{\text{Experimental Yield}}{\text{Theoretical Yield}} \times 100\%$$

1.11 Learning Check

1. *A student determines that the theoretical yield of her preparation of aspirin should produce 4.3 g of product. After drying and weighing her product, she obtained 3.8 g. What was her percent yield?*

2. *Sodium thiosulphate may be produced by boiling solid sulphur, $S_8(s)$ in a solution of sodium nitrite, $Na_2SO_3(aq)$, according to the reaction*

$$S_8(s) + 8Na_2SO_3(aq) \rightarrow 8Na_2S_2O_3(aq)$$

If a student starts with 15.50 g of sulphur and an excess of Na_2SO_3, determine the theoretical yield of product. If only 500 g of product is collected, determine the percent yield.

Empirical & Molecular Formulae

A formula is simply the molar ratio of elements in a compound. Water has 2 moles of hydrogen for every mole of oxygen. This ratio is fixed for a given compound. If you have a compound of 2 moles of hydrogen for 2 moles of oxygen, you don't have water; you have hydrogen peroxide – a compound with properties different from water.

As long as we know the ratio of the elements in any units, we can convert to moles and we can determine the empirical formula.

Lots of time these questions show up on Paper 1, and that's a good thing. Because you can't have a calculator, you must be given information in simple multiples of the relative mass.

What is the empirical formula of a compound that contains 46 g of sodium, 64 g of sulphur and 48 g of oxygen?   Classic Question

If you look at the periodic table, you notice that the molar masses are 23, 32, and 16 respectively. Therefore you must have 2 moles of sodium, 2 moles of sulphur and 3 moles of oxygen. $Na_2S_2O_3$!

Which of the following compounds has the greatest empirical mass?   Classic Question

a) C_6H_6 b) $C_{20}H_{40}$ c) C_4H_{10} d) CH_3

Solution: (c)-the empirical formulae are CH, CH_2, C_2H_5 and CH_3 respectively

Calculations from percentage by mass information

Steps: Problem solving
                                                                                          steps
1) Assume 100 g of compound – therefore %'s become grams.

2) Convert grams to moles by dividing by the molar mass.

3) Convert the ratio against 1 by dividing by the smallest value.

Compound Q is analysed and found to contain 85.6% carbon and 14.4% hydrogen by mass. Determine the empirical formula of Q.   Example

Process	Carbon	Hydrogen
Information	85.6% carbon	14.4%
Assume 100g	85.6 g	14.4 g
Divide by M_r	85.6 g ÷ 12.01= 7.13 mol	14.4 g ÷ 1.01 = 14.26 mol
divide by smallest	7.13 ÷ 7.13	14.26 ÷ 7.13 = 1.999
ratio	1	2

The formula of compound Q is therefore CH_2.

Formulae that do not have a ratio against one. For example, Fe_2O_3.   Be Careful
If you do the previous calculations, and you find that at the end, you have a formula of 1:1.5, then you will have to double all subscripts to attain a whole number ratio.

Try the following.   1.12 Learning
1. *Compound X is analysed and found to contain 82.63% carbon and   Check
    17.37% hydrogen. Determine the empirical formula of X.*

2. *If compound Y contains 89.92% carbon and 10.08% hydrogen. What is the empirical formula of compound Y?*

3. *What is the empirical formula of a compound containing 92.24% carbon and 7.76% hydrogen?*

Calculations from Empirical Data

Instead of being given the ratio of elements in terms of a percentage, we may be given masses of combustion products. We can convert to moles from the molar masses of the combustion products.

Because carbon dioxide contains one mole of carbon for every mole of CO_2, that will be easy. We must remember that water contains 2 moles of hydrogen for every mole of water, so we must double the number moles of water to determine the number of moles of hydrogen.

Problem solving steps

1) Determine the number of moles of carbon from carbon dioxide.

2) Determine the number of moles of hydrogen from water (multiply by 2).

3) Convert the ratio against 1 by dividing by the smallest number of moles.

4) Clear any fractions if necessary.

Example

A sample of a hydrocarbon with a mass of 2.37 g was burned in excess O_2 to produce 7.18 g of CO_2 and 3.67 g of H_2O. What is the empirical formula of the hydrocarbon?

Solution

Thought Process	carbon solution	hydrogen solution
Determine moles of combustion products CO_2 & H_2O	$n_{CO_2} = \dfrac{7.18\ g}{44.01 gmol^{-1}}$ $n_{CO_2} = 0.163\ mol$	$n_{H_2O} = \dfrac{3.67\ g}{18.02\ gmol^{-1}}$ $n_{H_2O} = 0.204\ mol$
moles of elements (double for hydrogen)	$n_C = 0.163\ mol$	$n_H = 2 \times 0.204\ mol$ $n_H = 0.408\ mol$
divide by smallest	0.163 mol ÷ 0.163 = 1	0.408 mol ÷ 0.163 = 2.50
clear fraction (x2)	2	5

The empirical formula is therefore C_2H_5!

1.13 Learning Check

1. *2.75 g of a compound containing only carbon and hydrogen were combusted. The combustion products were 8.05 g of CO_2 and 4.94 g of H_2O. Determine the empirical formula of the compound.*

2. *0.875 g of a hydrocarbon were burned in excess oxygen and produced 2.74 g of CO_2 and 1.12 g of water. What is the formula of the hydrocarbon?*

3. *A hydrocarbon sample of mass 1.15 g is completely combusted to form 3.44 g of carbon dioxide and 1.88 g of water. Determine the empirical formula of the sample.*

Compounds containing oxygen

If you have been given percentage information, then you can work as before but now you have three elements to deal with.
However if you are given empirical data, it's not so easy.
The problem is that you have to determine the number of moles of oxygen in the compound, but that the presence of oxygen gas for combustion is confounding because the oxygen present in the two products has come from two sources.

$$C_xH_yO_z + O_2(g) \rightarrow CO_2(g) + H_2O(g)$$

The solution, therefore, is to ignore the amount of oxygen in the products and calculate the amount of oxygen in the fuel (reactant) by subtracting what we do know – the carbon and the hydrogen – from the starting mass.

Let's use the combustion of ethanol, C_2H_6O, as a known example.

A sample of 2.35 g of compound containing C, H and O, is combusted in an excess of oxygen to produce 4.49 g of CO_2 and 2.75 g of H_2O. Determine the formula of the compound.   Example

Thought Process	carbon solution	hydrogen solution	oxygen solution
Determine moles of combustion products CO_2 & H_2O	$n_{CO_2} = \dfrac{4.49\text{ g}}{44.01\text{gmol}^{-1}}$ $n_{CO_2} = 0.102$ mol	$n_{H_2O} = \dfrac{2.75\text{ g}}{18.02\text{ gmol}^{-1}}$ $n_{H_2O} = 0.153$ mol	
moles of elements (double for H)	$n_C = 0.102$ mol	$n_H = 2 \times 0.153$ mol $n_H = 0.305$ mol	
Mass of element from compound Subtract for oxygen.	$m_C = 0.102 \times 12.01$ $m_C = 1.23$ g	$m_H = 0.305 \times 1.01$ $m_H = 0.308$ g	$m_O = 2.35$ g $-(1.23g + 0.308g)$ $m_O = 0.812$
moles of elements	as above $n_C = 0.102$ mol	as above $n_H = 0.305$ mol	$n_O = 0.812 \div 16.00$ $n_O = 0.0508$ mol
divide by smallest	0.102 mol ÷ 0.0508 = 2	0.305 mol ÷ 0.0508 = 6	0.0508 mol ÷ 0.0508 = 1
mole ratio	2	6	1

Therefore the formula (as expected) is C_2H_6O.

1.14 Learning Check

1. *4.35 g of a compound containing carbon, oxygen and hydrogen were combusted and the products were 6.38 g of carbon dioxide and 2.61 g of water. What was the empirical formula of the compound?*

2. *An alcohol of mass 2.63 g was completely combusted in an excess of oxygen. The products were found to be 5.78 g of CO_2 and 3.15 g of H_2O. Determine the empirical formula of the compound.*

3. *One gram of a carboxylic acid is analysed by combustion and the reaction produced 2.00 g of CO_2 and 0.818 g of H_2O. What is the empirical formula of the acid?*

Molecular Formula

The empirical formula represents the simplest ratio of elements. Usually molecules are more complex.
The molecular formula is an integer multiple of the empirical formula. Below are two examples for CH_2 and CH_2O empirical formulae.

Empirical Formula	CH_2	CH_2O	1
Possible Molecular Formulae	C_2H_4	$C_2H_4O_2$	2
	C_3H_6	$C_3H_6O_3$	3
	C_4H_8	$C_4H_8O_4$	4
	C_5H_{10}	$C_5H_{10}O_5$	5
	C_6H_{12}	$C_6H_{12}O_6$	6

Table 1.5: Relationship between empirical and molecular formulae

Be Careful!

The empirical formula is different from the general formula for organic compounds.

You are often asked to determine the molecular formula once you have determined the empirical formula (or the information is given). You only need one more piece of information - the molar (or molecular) mass.

The key is to find the mass of the empirical unit. The molar mass must be a whole number multiple of the empirical mass.

Empirical Mass	CH_2 = 14	CH_2O = 30	1
Possible Molecular Formulae masses	C_2H_4 = 28 (2 x 14)	$C_2H_4O_2$ = 60 (2 x 30)	2
	C_3H_6 = 42 (3 x 14)	$C_3H_6O_3$ = 90 (3 x 30)	3
	C_4H_8 = 56 (4 x 14)	$C_4H_8O_4$ = 120 (4 x 30)	4
	C_5H_{10} = 60 (5 x 14)	$C_5H_{10}O_5$ = 150 (5 x 30)	5
	C_6H_{12} = 74 (6 x 14)	$C_6H_{12}O_6$ = 180 (6 x 30)	6

Table 1.6: Empirical Mass Relationships

Summary Questions

1. 250 cm³ of a solution of unknown concentration of sodium chloride.
   20 cm³ sample is removed and reacted with excess silver nitrate causing a white precipitate.
   When washed and dried, the precipitate had a mass of 0.430 g.
   a) Write the balanced equation including state symbols.
   b) Determine the moles of precipitate, and hence the moles of sodium chloride in 20 cm³.
   c) Determine the concentration of the solution.
   d) What mass of sodium chloride was used to make the original solution?

2. Calcium carbide, $CaC_2(s)$ reacts with water to produce a flammable hydrocarbon gas, and
   calcium hydroxide.
   0.0405 g of the gas has a volume of 38.65 cm³ at 22.00°C and 98.00 kPa.
   Upon combustion the same amount of gas produces 0.137 g of CO_2 and 0.0280 g of H_2O.
   a) Determine the empirical formula of the gas.
   b) Determine the number of moles and hence the molar mass of the gas.
   c) Determine the molecular formula.
   d) Write a balanced equation for the reaction of calcium carbide with water.

3. Aspririn may be be prepared by the reaction of salicylic acid, $C_7H_6O_3$ with ethanoic anhydride,
   $C_4H_6O_3$ according to the reaction

$$C_7H_6O_3 + C_4H_6O_3 \ \rightarrow \ C_9H_8O_4 + CH_3COOH$$

   If 6.00 g of salicylic acid and 5.00 g of ethanoic anhydride are reacted.
   a) Determine the moles of each reactant.
   b) Determine the limiting reactant.
   c) Determine the mass of product that should be produced.
   d) If a student only recovers 6.50 g of aspirin, calculate the theoretical yield.

4. Hexane, C_6H_{14}, is a combustible hydrocarbon. Consider the combustion of a mixture of 4.50
   g of hexane and 11.25 g of oxygen.
   a) Write the balanced equation for the reaction
   b) Determine the moles of each reactant.
   c) Determine the limiting reactant.
   d) Determine the mass of each, carbon dioxide and water produced.
   e) Determine the mass of excess reactant.

5. A metal sulphate has the formula M_2SO_4. 10.99 g of the compound was dissolved in water to
   make 500 cm³ of solution. A 25.00 cm³ sample was removed and reacted with an excess of
   $BaCl_2(aq)$ to produce a precipitate of $BaSO_4(s)$, which, when dried had a mass of 1.167 g.
   a) Determine the number of moles of $BaSO_4(s)$ precipitated.
   b) Determine the concentration of the M_2SO_4 solution.
   c) Determine the number of moles of M_2SO_4 in the original solution.
   d) Determine the molar mass of M_2SO_4.
   e) Determine the identity of M.

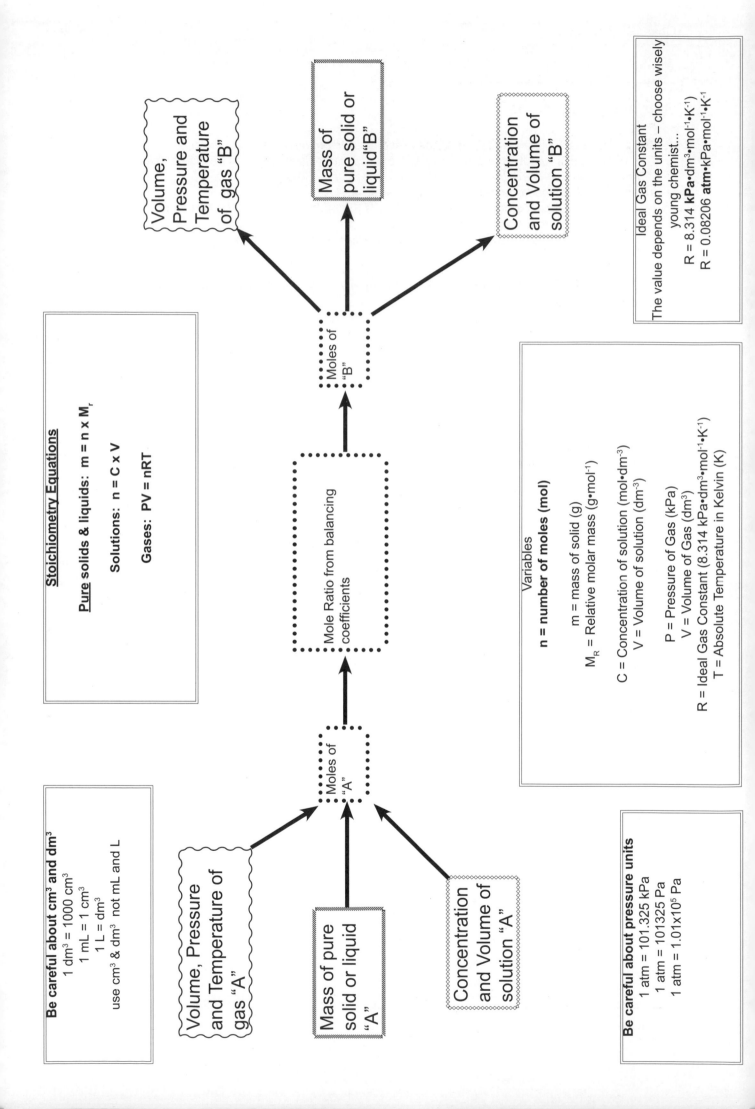

CHAPTER 2

ATOMIC STRUCTURE

Subatomic Particles

Atoms are made up of 3 subatomic particles – know their properties…

Particle	Relative Mass	Relative Charge	Location
Proton	1	+1	Nucleus
Neutron	1	0 (neutral)	Nucleus
Electron	5×10^{-4}	-1	Orbiting nucleus

Table 2.1: Subatomic Particles

The protons and neutrons give the nucleus and hence the atoms their mass, while the electron orbits give the atoms their volume.

The number of protons is unique for a given element, or if you like, the way we identify elements is by the number of protons.
The number of neutrons can be different, which gives rise to different isotopes.
The number of electrons can change during the course of a chemical reaction as atoms gain or lose electrons to form different ions or oxidation states.

The Nuclear Atom & Isotopes

Isotopes are... (here are two ways to say the same thing...)

Definition

> _atoms_ with the same number of protons with a different number of neutrons.
>
> _atoms_ of the same element with different masses.

Get the point!   you must say that isotopes are **ATOMS**.

Thinking: There isn't one or "real" or "true" atom and the others are isotopes. There may be one isotope that is more ABUNDANT – there is a greater percentage of that one compared to others.
Most elements have multiple isotopes, but not all. Fluorine, for instance has only one naturally occurring isotope – Fluorine-19. Chlorine has two, Chlorine-35 and Chlorine-37
As a teacher I always like to ask questions about isotopes that have a different mass from the one on the periodic table – I always catch at least one student saying: "I think this question is wrong."

Isotopes differ from each other due to the change in mass (only). Isotopes may have slightly different physical properties - ^2H_2O has a boiling point of 101.4°C. Diffusion is also a common property that changes because the heavier isotopes will move more slowly.

Isotopes have the same chemical properties because the chemical properties are determined by the nuclear charge and electronic structure, not the mass.

Isotope Notation

$$^A_Z X$$

Where Z is the number of protons and A is the number of protons plus neutrons. At the moment, we will deal with neutral atoms, so electrons=protons.

Complete the following table

2.1 Learning Check

Isotope symbol	Atomic Mass (A)	Atomic Number (Z)	Protons	Neutrons	Electrons
$^{23}_{11}$Na	23	11	11	12	11
$^{1}_{1}$H	1	1	1	0	1
$^{2}_{1}$H	2	1	1	1	1
$^{3}_{1}$H	3	1	1	2	1
$^{10}_{5}$B	10	5	5	5	5
$^{11}_{5}$B	11	5	5	6	5
$^{35}_{17}$Cl	35	17	17	18	17
$^{37}_{17}$Cl	37	17	17	20	17

The Mass Spectrometer

The mass spectrometer is a device that separates particles based on their mass. In order for the particles to move through the device, they must be positively charged ions.

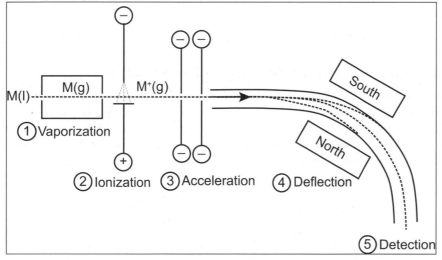

Figure 2.2: Schematic of a Mass Spectrometer

1) Vaporization – *heat to turn the substance into a gas.*
2) Ionization – *by bombardment of high-energy electrons to knock out an electron forming a positive ion.*
3) Acceleration – *by an **electric** field.*
4) Deflection – *by a **magnetic** field.*
5) Detection – *of ions, but no need to learn how this is done.*

Get the point!   Know the order of the stages and the process by which they occur.
                   The product of the mass spectrometer is the mass spectrum, which shows
                   the relative abundance of the isotopes.

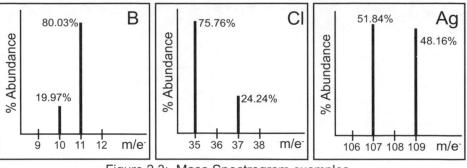

Figure 2.3: Mass Spectrogram examples

Relative Atomic Mass

Definition

> Carbon-12, which has 6 protons, 6 neutrons and 6 electrons is defined as
> having a relative atomic mass of exactly 12.000.
>
> One "atomic mass unit" (amu or u) is defined as 1/12 of this mass.

All other isotopes are measured compared to this value.

Average Relative Atomic Mass

The average Relative Atomic mass (A_r) is the weighted average for all
isotopes of a given element based upon their relative percent abundance. eg.
If two isotopes are present in equal amounts, then the average atomic mass
is going to be the simple average.
If one isotope is present in a greater proportion, it counts more to the
average.

The average relative mass is what you read off of the periodic table.

Calculating Relative Average Atomic Mass

You need to multiply each atomic mass by its relative abundance and add the
numbers up!

Example   *Chlorine exists as two naturally occurring isotopes; Cl-35 and Cl-37. If the
                   Cl-35 has an abundance of 75.76% and the remainder is Cl-37, determine
                   the relative average atomic mass of chlorine.*

$$A_r = \frac{Mass_{isotope(1)} \times \%abudance + Mass_{isotope(2)} \times}{100}$$

$$A_r = \frac{(35 \times 75.76\%) + (37 \times 24.24\%)}{100}$$

$$A_r = 35.48$$

2.2 Learning   1. *Silver has 2 naturally occurring stable isotopes, in the following ratios:
Check   ^{107}Ag: 51.84% and ^{109}Ag: 48.16%. Determine the relative average atomic
                     mass of silver.*

2. *Magnesium has three naturally occurring isotopes, in the following abundances: ^{24}Mg: 79.0%, ^{25}Mg: 10.0%, ^{26}Mg: 11.0%. Calculate the relative average atomic mass of magnesium.*

3. *Boron exists as 19.97% ^{10}B and 80.03% ^{11}B. Determine the Ar.*

Calculating Natural Abundance

Calculating Natural abundance isn't really a chemistry question, it's a math question.

Let's take a common example - chlorine.

Chlorine exists as two isotopes - ^{35}Cl and ^{37}Cl. If the average atomic mass is 35.45, calculate the percentage calculation for each isotope.   Example

    Solution

    Let the fraction of Cl-37 be x
    Then the fraction of Cl-35 will be (1-x)

    37x + 35(1-x) = 35.5
    37x + 35-35x = 35.5
    2x = 0.5
    x=0.25

Therefore ^{37}Cl has 25% abundance, and ^{35}Cl has the rest - 75%

1. *Thallium consists of thallium-203 and thallium-205. Using the value from the periodic table, determine the relative abundance of each isotope.*   2.3 Learning
                                                                                    Check

2. *Lithium consists of ^{6}Li and ^{7}Li. Calculate the percent ratio of the isotopes.*

3. *Gallium is made up of ^{69}Ga and ^{71}Ga. Determine the isotopic ratio using the average value from the periodic table.*

The Electronic Atom - Basic structure

Now that you have studied the nucleus with the two "nucleons" – protons and neutrons, we look at the structure of the atom in terms of electrons. Electrons are arranged in shells or orbits or layers.
All of chemistry is governed by electrostatic attraction – that is + and – charges.

Evidence for Structure – the Hydrogen spectrum

Definition

> *A continuous spectrum contains **all** the wavelengths / frequencies / colour or **ENERGIES** of electromagnetic radiation (not just light)*

Low Energy ──────────────→ High Energy

Figure 2.4: A Continuous Spectrum

Definition

> *A line spectrum contains **only certain** / specific / discreet wavelengths / frequencies / colours or **ENERGIES** of electromagnetic radiation.*

When we observe hydrogen in a discharge tube, we see a line spectrum, not a continuous spectrum.

Low Energy ──────────────→ High Energy

Figure 2.5: The Hydrogen Emission Line Spectrum

Explaining the Hydrogen Spectrum.

In hydrogen atoms the electron is in its ground state when the single electron is as close to the nucleus as possible – the first shell.
The electron can be given extra energy by a fast moving electron in the discharge tube, and this causes it to be promoted to a higher energy level.
Due to attraction to the nucleus, the electron "falls" back down.
The difference in energy levels (shells) is the same amount of energy as the energies seen in the line spectrum.
Because the electron can only be in certain places (shells) we only see certain colours. If the electron were allowed to be anywhere, we would see the continuous spectrum!

Stage 1 - Ground State	Stage 2 - Excited State	Stage 3 - Ground State
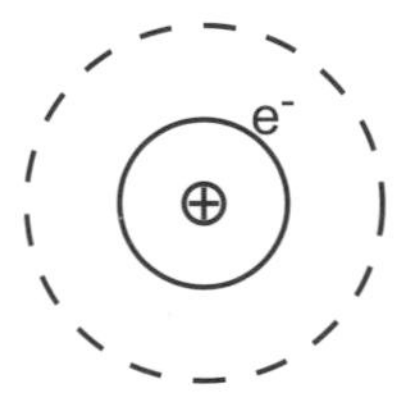	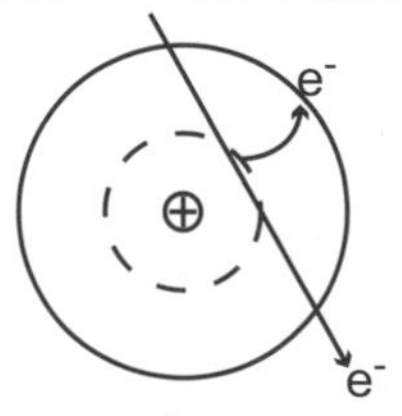	
Orbiting electron is in the ground state, nearest to the nucleus, due to attraction	Electron is knocked up to a higher energy state by collision of a fast moving electron	Electron returns to the ground state and releases extra energy in the form of light.

Figure 2.6: Electronic Transitions in Hydrogen

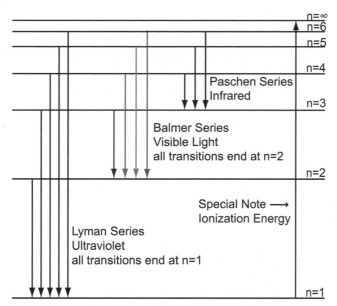

Figure 2.7: Energy Level Transitions

If you look carefully at both the hydrogen emission spectrum and the energy level transitions above, you will notice that as you get towards a higher energy level, the levels converge.

Successive Ionization Energies – evidence for shells

As successive electrons are removed from the atom, we see that there is a disproportionate jump as one of the electrons is removed. This jump in ionization energy represents the removal of an electron from a shell closer to the nucleus than the previous electrons removed.

Ionization Eneries / kJ mol^{-1}						
Element	I_1	I_2	I_3	I_4	I_5	I_6	I_7
Na	495	**4560**					
Mg	735	1445	**7730**				
Al	580	1815	2740	**11600**			
Si	780	1575	3220	4350	**16100**		
P	1060	1890	2905	4950	6270	**21200**	
S	1005	2260	3375	4565	6950	8490	**27000**
Cl	1255	2295	2850	5160	6560	9360	11000
Ar	1527	2665	3945	5770	7230	8780	12000

Figure 2.8: Successive Ionization Energies

Look at silicon as an example; the first four ionization energies follow a trend, and the ionization energy takes a significant jump at the fifth one. This shows that the fifth electron is disproportionately harder to remove. We infer that the fifth electron is in a shell closer to the nucleus.

$$Si(g) \rightarrow Si^+(g) + e^- \qquad \Delta H_{first\ I.E} = 780\ kJ \cdot mol^{-1}$$
$$Si^+(g) \rightarrow Si^{2+}(g) + e^- \qquad \Delta H_{second\ I.E} = 1575\ kJ \cdot mol^{-1}$$
$$Si^{2+}(g) \rightarrow Si^{3+}(g) + e^- \qquad \Delta H_{third\ I.E} = 3220\ kJ \cdot mol^{-1}$$
$$Si^{3+}(g) \rightarrow Si^{4+}(g) + e^- \qquad \Delta H_{fourth\ I.E} = 4350\ kJ \cdot mol^{-1}$$
$$Si^{4+}(g) \rightarrow Si^{5+}(g) + e^- \qquad \Delta H_{fifth\ I.E} = 16100\ kJ \cdot mol^{-1}$$

We'll see more about ionization energy in Chapter 3.

Summary Questions

1. Determine the average atomic mass of element "Q" given the following data:
^{109}Q: 65.50%, ^{110}Q: 25.00%, ^{112}Q: 9.500%.

2. What is the natural abundance of each of ^{89}Lm and ^{90}Lm if the average relative mass is 89.65?

3. Write the electron configuration for the following species…
   a) P
   b) Se
   c) Br$^-$
   d) Ca^{2+}
   e) Ni^{2+}

4. Describe the processes that occur to give rise to a line spectrum

CHAPTER 3

PERIODICITY

IN THIS CHAPTER...

Structure of the Periodic Table

The periodic table is simply a listing of the elements in order of atomic number (number of protons).

The vertical columns are called "groups" or "families", the horizontal rows are called periods. Groups have similar chemical properties.

Groups have the same number of outer (valence) electrons – Group 1 (alkali metals) all have one valence electron.

Periods represent the filling of a valence shell. Sodium, for example, has 3 shells, with one electron in the outer shell, whereas chlorine has 3 shells with 7 electrons in the valence shell.

Figure 3.1: Structure of the Periodic Table

Physical Properties

In all the cases below, questions are designed to have one variable change, and all others remain the same. Your job in creating an answer is to correctly identify both of these. All of the physical properties depend ultimately on the balance of electrostatic attractions between oppositely charged particles (notice I didn't say protons & electrons) and the energy required to overcome these attractions. – Physics teachers will get on my case for comparing forces and energy.

In answering all these types of questions you must have a *logical sequence of thought*. The explanation must start with the physical reality, discuss the factors which are changing, and those which are staying the same. The changing factor must relate to a force of attraction between the relevant parts of the atom, and then finally how that force manifests itself with regards to the physical property under scrutiny.

Effective Nuclear Charge, Z_{eff}

Not examined by IBO, but it is valuable because it can help you understand the following properties. I'll explain it once here, and leave it to you to apply it later on.

The effective nuclear charge, Z_{eff}, arithmetically combines the positive charge of the nucleus and the negative charges of the core electrons (non-valence electrons).

eg. Magnesium has a Z_{eff} of 2+ due to 12 protons and 10 core electrons
Fluorine has a Z_{eff} of 7+ due to 9 protons, and only 2 inner electrons.

When working through the following trends, think about how the Z_{eff} is changing (or not)

Trends in the Periodic Table - The Basic Idea

All electrons, but most importantly the valence electrons, are held in orbit by the attractive force of the nucleus. That force depends on two factors - the charge on the nucleus, and the distance between the electrons and the nucleus.

$$\text{Force of attraction} = \frac{\text{nuclear charge}}{\text{distance}^2}$$

As you move across a period (in order of increasing atomic number), the number of protons in the nucleus increases, thus increasing the positive charge of the nucleus, which makes it more attractive to electrons. The increase of valence electrons does not contribute as much as the proton increase. (Think about Z_{eff})

As you move down a group, the number of electron shells increases, which increases the distance between the valence electron and the nucleus, which decreases the force of attraction between the nucleus and the valence electrons. The addition of protons in the nucleus is cancelled out by the shielding of core electrons. (Again, you can think about Z_{eff} if you want.)

Atomic Radius

Atomic Radius is really quite straightforward – it's a measure of the size of the atom.

Once again, the forces within the atom are simple electrostatic – opposites attract and likes repel. So, the valence electrons are attracted by the nucleus and repelled by other electrons – both those in the same shell and those in the underlying shells.

As the atomic number increases across the periodic table (left to right), the only (significant) thing that is changing is the charge on the nucleus – there are more protons. The increased number of protons causes an increase in the attractive force between the valence electron and the nucleus. With increased force comes decreased distance.

Below you can see the general trend of the radius decreasing along a period and increasing down a group.

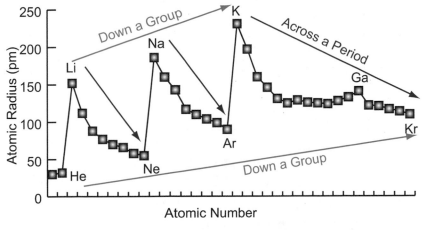

Figure 3.2: Atomic Radius vs. Atomic Number

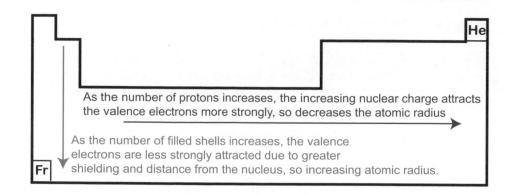

As the number of protons increases, the increasing nuclear charge attracts the valence electrons more strongly, so decreases the atomic radius

As the number of filled shells increases, the valence electrons are less strongly attracted due to greater shielding and distance from the nucleus, so increasing atomic radius.

Ionic Radius

The definition is effectively the same, but now we are talking about ions. Be careful to identify the electronic structure you are dealing with. Often you are asked to compare radii of positive and negative ions - sometimes with the same electron configuration, sometimes, with a whole shell difference!

Isoelectronic species

Isoelectronic just means particles with the same (exactly) electron number and therefore configuration. – This is actually quite easy, because 99% of the time, isoelectronic species are those ions that you probably learned before you started IB Chemistry. Isoelectronic species almost always have the noble gas electron configuration.

O^{2-}, F^-, Ne, Na^+, Mg^{2+} are isoelectronic – so what's the bit that's different? The protons of course – therefore Mg^{2+} with 12 protons is going have greater nuclear charge attracting the 10 electrons compared to O^{2-} with its 8 protons attracting 10 electrons.

	O	F	Ne	Na	Mg
protons	8	9	10	11	12
electrons	8	9	10	11	12
e- config.	2,6	2,7	2,8	2,8,1	2,8,2
radius	66	58	54	186	160

Table 3.3: Atomic Radii of 5 elements

	O^{2-}	F^-	Ne	Na^+	Mg^{2+}
protons	8	9	10	11	12
electrons	10	10	10	10	10
e- config.	2,8	2,8	2,8	2,8	2,8
radius	146	133	54	98	65

Table 3.4: Ionic Radii of 5 isoelectronic species

Atomic vs. Ionic Radii

What happens when an atom becomes an ion?

Short answer – positive ions are smaller because they lose shells, negative ions are bigger because they gain repulsive forces.

How much detail do you really need to give – have a look at the points for the answer. IB questions are often "State and explain..." – therefore 2 points. So your explanation doesn't need to be verbose.

Refer to your data book and see if you can justify the following ionic radii

Pair	Larger	Explanation
O / O^{2-}	O^{2-}	
Mg / Mg^{2+}		3 shells of electrons vs. 2 shells.
Ne / F$^-$		lower net attractive force for same no. of electrons
K / Ar	K	
K$^+$ / Ar	Ar	
Li / Na		
O / N		

3.1 Learning Check

Arrange the following groups in order of increasing size.

     a)   Be, Mg, Ca,
     b)   Te, I, Xe
     c)   Ga, Ge, In
     d)   As, N, F
     e)   S, Cl, F
     f)   Cs, Li, K

3.2 Learning Check

In each of the following sets, choose atom or ion that has the smallest radius? Justify your choices.

     a)   Li, Na, K
     b)   P, As
     c)   O$^+$, O, O$^-$
     d)   S, Cl, Kr
     e)   Pt, Pd, Ni
     f)   S^{2-}, Cl$^-$, Ar

3.3 Learning Check

Strange questions

Many times, you are asked questions which involve uncommon species as below. See if you can identify and explain the larger of the two species.

Pair	Larger	Explanation
Mg$^+$ / Mg^{2+}		
O$^+$ / O$^-$		
Ar / Ar$^+$		
Na$^+$ / Mg$^+$		
Al^{2+} / Mg^{2+}		

3.4 Learning Check

Ionization Energy

Definition

> *The energy required to remove one mole of electrons from one mole of neutral gaseous atoms.*

Let's look at the definition…

Why the mole thing?   It means that it will agree with the data booklet for quantities with kJ•mol⁻¹ for units. – You could talk about single atoms, but then you can't say "moles"

Why neutral?   It means it's the first electron to come off from an **atom**, not an ion.

Why gaseous?   That's because gaseous atoms are "infinitely" separated from their neighbours, and therefore do not have any confounding attractive forces – each atom is on its own.

So what are the factors that affect ionization energy? – Simple – the force of attraction between the valence electron and the nucleus. The stronger the force, the more energy is required to pull it away.

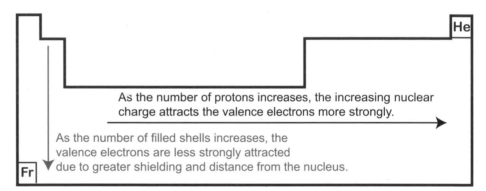

Figure 3.5: Trends in Ionization Energy

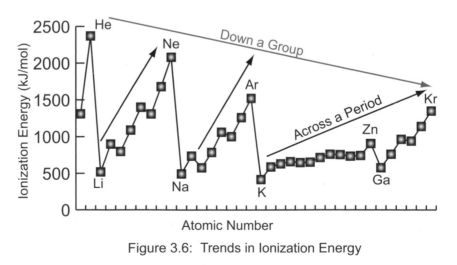

Figure 3.6: Trends in Ionization Energy

3.5 Learning Check   *Arrange the atoms in Learning Check 3.2 in order of increasing first ionization energy.*

A note about energy levels. Why is it that an electron in a higher energy level takes less energy to remove? Because it is closer to the "infinite" energy level (total removal). See Figure 2.7

Electronegativity

> *Electronegativity is the ability of an atom to attract a shared (bonding) pair of electrons.*   Definition

The Noble gases (He, Ne, Ar etc.) are not assigned any electronegativity values because they (usually) do not form bonds.
This is really only useful later on for figuring out what type of bond you have. Large differences in electronegativity mean that the bond will be ionic; medium differences mean that it will be polar covalent, and small differences – covalent. See Table 4.1

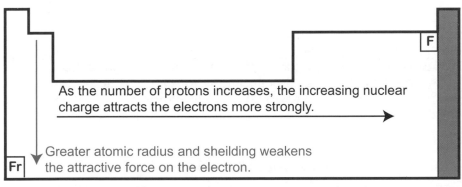

As the number of protons increases, the increasing nuclear charge attracts the electrons more strongly.

Greater atomic radius and sheilding weakens the attractive force on the electron.

Figure 3.7: Trends in Electronegativity

Melting Points

First read about intermolecular forces in the Bonding chapter.

The melting point is the temperature that gives the particles enough kinetic energy so that they can overcome the attractive forces acting in the lattice of the solid crystal.

Melting points are a measure of the attractive forces that hold the lattice together.

Melting does not decompose a compound into its elements - it is only a change of state!

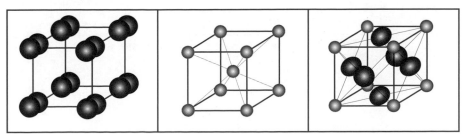

Figure 3.8:   Some Lattice Structures

Melting points of Group I – The alkali metals

Before we discuss the melting point, we must recall the type of bonding – in this case metallic.

Metallic bonding is the attractive force between the lattice of positive ions, and the "sea" of delocalized electrons. There are three factors affecting the strength of the attraction

Know it!

1) – The charge on the ion (eg. +1, +2, +3 for Na, Mg, and Al respectively)
2) – The number of delocalized electrons (the opposite charge as the ion)
3) – The size of the ion. – as the ions increases in size, the charge density decreases.

Element	Charge	Radius / pm	Melting point (K)
Li	+1	152	454
Na	+1	186	371
K	+1	231	337
Rb	+1	244	312
Cs	+1	262	302

Table 3.9: Melting Points of the Alkali Metals

You can get two points for one comment – "*charge density*". As the ion gets larger, the charge is diluted over the increased surface of the ionic sphere. As the charge density decreases, the force of attraction between the ion and the delocalized electrons is lowered, therefore the melting point lowers.

Melting points of Group VII – The Halogens

The solid halogens have non-polar diatomic molecules at their lattice points. The attractive forces holding the lattice together therefore are van der Waals' forces or London Dispersion Forces. How do van der Waals' forces change as one looks down the group? – They increase due to increased molecular mass / molecular size / number of electrons – there are a variety of explanations.

Diatomic element	State at 25°C	Mass (diatomic molecules X_2)	Number of electrons	Melting point (K)
F_2	Gas	38.00	18	54
Cl_2	Gas	70.90	34	172
Br_2	Liquid	159.8	70	266
I_2	Solid	253.8	106	387

Table 3.10: Melting Points of the Halogens

Melting points across period 3

The secret here is to break the horizontal period into 3 or 4 sections, according to the type of bonding present.

Na	Mg	Al	Si	P_4	S_8	Cl_2	Ar
Metallic bonding			Giant Covalent	Molecular Covalent			Atoms
Increasing → due to greater ionic charge and increased number of delocalized electrons			Very strong covalent bonds between all atoms	S_8 is highest due to greater van der Waals' forces, then P_4, then Cl_2			Weak van der Waals' forces
371 K	922 K	936 K	1683 K	317 K	392 K	172 K	84 K

Table 3.11: Period 3 Bond types and Melting Points

Caution – phosphorus comes as P_4, sulphur as S_8, and you should know that chlorine is Cl_2.

Get the point!

Chemical Properties

Reactivity is the ability of an **element** to form a compound or an ion.
Very reactive elements are found in nature as ions (eg. sodium), unreactive elements are found as the element (eg. gold).
Metals react by giving away electrons, forming positive ions. Non-metals react by taking electrons, and forming negative ions.
We don't generally speak of the reactivity of ions - they are the products of the reaction that has already occurred.

Common Mistake

Reactions of Alkali Metals and Halogens

Alkali metals react with halogens to form their salts. Check you periodic table - the most vigorous reaction is between metals that lose electrons easily and halogens that are very good at taking electrons - eg. CsF.

$2Li(s) + Cl_2(g) \rightarrow 2LiCl(s)$	Increasing reactivity down the group, as metal atoms can lose their valence electron more easily.
$2Na(s) + Cl_2(g) \rightarrow 2NaCl(s)$	
$2K(s) + Cl_2(g) \rightarrow 2KCl(s)$	

Table 3.12: The formation of the chloride salts

Reactions of Alkali Metals with Water

Most students have seen or done these reactions. In all cases the product is a soluble base - called an alkali, and hydrogen gas.

$2Li(s) + 2H_2O(l) \rightarrow 2LiOH(aq) + H_2(g)$	slow reaction, bubbles produced
$2Na(s) + 2H_2O(l) \rightarrow 2NaOH(aq) + H_2(g)$	vigorous reaction, heat generated
$2K(s) + 2H_2O(l) \rightarrow 2KOH(aq) + H_2(g)$	violent, hydrogen catches fire

Table 3.13: The reactions of the alkali metals with water

Properties of the Halogens

Halogen	Colour in non-polar solvent	Colour in water
Cl_2	pale green/yellow	pale green/yellow
Br_2	reddish / orangy / brown	orangy/brown
I_2	purple / violet	dark straw (not very soluble)

Table 3.14: Identifying halogens by colour

Be careful!

Remember that the **halogens** are F_2, Cl_2, Br_2, I_2, and the hal*ide* ions are F^-, Cl^-, Br^-, I^-.
Many students mix them up. Be careful of the names!

Consider a halogen reacting with a halide ion. The ion has an extra electron, and the halogen has an affinity for electrons. Is the halogen strong enough to take the electron away from the halide ion? Maybe, it depends on their relative positions in the family.
Fluorine is the best electron taker, while iodine is the weakest.

If you consider the reactions of bromine (Br_2), it is able to remove electrons from the "weaker" iodide ion (I^-), but not the chloride ion, Cl^-.
See Table 3.15 for the complete series including colour changes.

	Reaction	colour of non-polar layer
a)	$Cl_2(aq) + 2Br^-(aq) \rightarrow 2Cl^-(aq) + Br_2(aq)$	green to orange
b)	$Cl_2(aq) + 2I^-(aq) \rightarrow 2Cl^-(aq) + I_2(aq)$	green to purple
c)	$Br_2(aq) + 2Cl^-(aq) \rightarrow$ no reaction	stays orange
d)	$Br_2(aq) + 2I^-(aq) \rightarrow 2Br^-(aq) + I_2(aq)$	orange to purple
e)	$I_2(aq) + 2Cl^-(aq) \rightarrow$ no reaction	stays purple
f)	$I_2(aq) + 2Cl^-(aq) \rightarrow$ no reaction	stays purple

Table 3.15: Reactions demonstrating the relative reactivity of the halogens

Reactions a), and d) are the two important ones, because they demonstrate best the relative reactivity with positive results.

Summary Questions

1. *In terms of electron configuration, outline the reasoning for the following observations…*
   a) *the first ionization energy of sulfur is less than phosphorus*
   b) *the first ionization energy of boron is greater than aluminium.*
   c) *the second ionization energy of sodium is greater than magnesium*

2. *State and explain the difference between…*
   a) *the atomic radius of nitrogen and oxygen.*
   b) *the atomic radius of nitrogen and phosphorus.*
   c) *the ionic radii of Si^{4+} and P^{3-}.*

3. *State and explain the trend in atomic radius and ionization energy of*
   a) *the alkali metals.*
   b) *the elements of period 3 Na to Ar.*

4. *Write balanced equations for the following reactions*
   a) *lithium and iodine*
   b) *potassium and water*
   c) *bromine and iodide*

CHAPTER 4

BONDING

Types of Bonding

In compounds there are really only 2 types of bonding – ionic and covalent – or as I like to say – electron transfer and electron sharing. The problem is that it's not black and white – it's grey. The type of bonding depends on the difference in electronegativity - Large differences in electronegativity mean that the bond will be ionic; medium differences mean that it will be polar covalent, and small differences will be covalent.

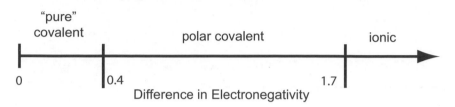

Figure 4.1: The Bonding Continuum

2.1																	He
1.0	1.5											2.0	2.5	3.0	3.5	4.0	Ne
0.9	1.2											1.5	1.8	2.1	2.5	3.0	Ar
0.8	1.0	1.3	1.5	1.6	1.6	1.5	1.8	1.8	1.8	1.9	1.6	1.6	1.8	2.0	2.4	2.8	Kr
0.8	0.9	1.2	1.4	1.6	1.8	1.9	2.2	2.2	2.2	1.9	1.7	1.7	1.8	1.9	2.1	2.5	Xe

Table 4.2: Values of Electronegativity in the Periodic Table

You don't really need to make the calculations, because you can generally make the following safe assumptions.

Metal – non-metal = ionic

Two different non metals = polar covalent

Two identical non-metals (Cl_2) = non-polar covalent bond (also C-H)

The greater the separation on the periodic table the greater the polarity.

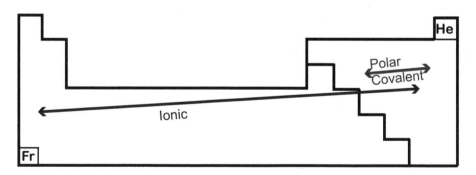

Figure 4.3: Relationship between separation and bond type

Ionic Charges & Formulae

1+	2+		3+	4+/4-	3-	2-	1-	0

1+	2+		3+	4+/4-	3-	2-	1-	0
H								He
Li	Be		B	C	N	O	F	Ne
Na	Mg		Al	Si	P	S	Cl	Ar
K	Ca		Ga	Ge	As	Se	Br	Xe

Is it +2 or 2+?

Officially, ionic charges are written as 2+ because they represent a multiple of positive (or negative) charge, whereas oxidation numbers are written as +2 because they represent an integer value.

The oxidation state of iron in *iron(III) oxide* is +3. It contains the Fe^{3+} ion.

Simple ionic compounds – from the periodic table

In order to write valid ionic formulae, there must be an overall charge of zero. All compounds are electrically neutral – the total of the positive charges must equal the total of the negative charges.

Consider the following compounds;

Compound	positive	negative	total +	total -	formula
lithium fluoride	Li^+	F^-	1+	-1	LiF
potassium oxide	K^+	O^{2-}	2(1+)	-2	K_2O
magnesium chloride	Mg^{2+}	Cl^-	2+	2(-1)	$MgCl_2$
calcium sulphide	Ca^{2+}	S^{2-}	2+	2-	CaS
aluminium chloride	Al^{3+}	Cl^-	3+	3(1-)	$AlCl_3$
aluminium oxide	Al^{3+}	O^{2-}	3+	2(1-)	Al_2O_3

Write the correct formulae for the following compounds.
- a) sodium sulphide
- b) beryllium fluoride
- c) gallium iodide
- d) potassium nitride
- e) aluminium phosphide
- f) magnesium nitride

4.1 Learning Check

Transition metal compounds

Transition metal compounds are even easier. Because there are multiple ions, you must be specific about which one you want. The oxidation state is given in Roman numerals in brackets.

If you are asked to name a compound, you must use the negative charge to figure out the charge on the positive ion and consequently its name.

Iron(II) chloride Fe^{2+} Cl^- $FeCl_2$
Iron(III) chloride Fe^{3+} Cl^- $FeCl_3$

FeO   O is 2- therefore iron must be 2+   iron(II) oxide
Fe_2O_3 negative charge is 6-, therefore EACH Fe is 3+; iron(III) oxide.

Name the following compounds.
- a) CuCl
- b) CoI_2
- c) Cr_2O_3
- d) $NiBr_3$
- e) MnO_2
- f) Cu_2S

4.2 Learning Check

4.3 Learning   *Write the formulae for the following compounds.*
Check
     a) *iron(II) oxide*   b) *mercury(II) chloride*   c) *copper(I) oxide*
     d) *nickel(III) oxide*   e) *cobalt(II) chloride*   f) *iron(III) sulphide*

Compounds of polyatomic ions.

A poly atomic ion is really just a charged molecule. That means that the ion itself is held together with covalent bonds, but because it has a charge overall, it is attracted by electrostatic forces to other ions.

Common IB poly atomic ions		Other ions	
Ammonia	NH_4^+		
Nitrate	NO_3^-	nitrite	NO_2^-
Carbonate	CO_3^{2-}	hydrogen carbonate	HCO_3^-
Sulphate	SO_4^{2-}	sulphite	SO_3^{2-}
Phosphate	PO_4^{3-}	phosphite	PO_3^{3-}

4.4 Learning   *Write correct formulae for the following compounds.*
Check
     a) *ammonium chloride*   b) *sodium nitrate*
     c) *potassium carbonate*   d) *calcium sulphate*
     e) *magnesium phosphate*   f) *ammonium carbonate*

4.5 Learning   *Name the following compounds.*
Check
     a) $NaHCO_3$ b) $NaNO_2$ c) NH_4NO_3
     d) Li_3PO_4 e) $BaSO_4$ f) $(NH_4)_2SO_4$

4.6 Learning   *Write correct formulae for the following compounds.*
Check
     a) *iron(II) sulphate*   b) *nickel(III) nitrate*
     c) *chromium(VI) nitrate*   d) *copper(I) carbonate*
     e) *mercury(II) nitrate*   f) *manganese(II) sulphate*

4.7 Learning   *Name the following compounds.*
Check
     a) $NiCO_3$ b) $CuSO_4$ c) $Fe_2(SO_4)_3$
     d) $Co(NO_3)_2$ e) $Ni(NO_3)_3$ f) Hg_2CO_3

Covalent Formulae

The following molecules and shapes are identified in the syllabus as ones to know. Know them!

Name	Formula	Lewis Structure	comment
oxygen	O_2	$\ddot{O} = \ddot{O}$	~20% of air
nitrogen	N_2	$:N \equiv N:$	~80% of air
carbon dioxide	CO_2	$\ddot{O} = C = \ddot{O}$	you breathe out, plants "breathe" in
hydrogen cyanide	HCN	$H - C \equiv N:$	very poisonous
ethane	C_2H_6	(structure)	a flammable hydrocarbon gas
ethene	C_2H_4	(structure)	contains a double bond that can react
ethyne	C_2H_2	$H - C \equiv C - H$	contains a triple bond

Table 4.4: Some common covalent molecules

If you are asked to draw the Lewis structure of an unfamiliar compound, then you need to build from your knowledge of the periodic table.

Lewis Structure

A Lewis structure shows all electrons either as a bonding pair or a lone pair (non-bonding pair). In order to draw a proper Lewis structure you must follow these steps...

1. Count the total number of valence electrons.

2. Adjust for charge (remember negative charges ADD electrons).

3. Connect atoms to central atom with lines representing 2 electrons.

4. Complete the octet on surrounding atoms (except hydrogen of course).

5. Place extra electrons on the central atom.

6. Ensure octet rule satisfaction by moving lone pairs to form double or triple bonds if necessary.

7. Draw the molecule or ion as clearly as possible to show the shape.

8. If you are drawing an ion, put the species in square brackets and indicate the charge outside the brackets.

Problem solving steps

Draw the Lewis structure for CCl_4, NF_3, H_2O and CO_2.

	CCl_4	NF_3	H_2O	CO_2
# of electrons	4+4(7) = 32	5+3(7) =26	2(1)+6 = 8	4+2(6)=16
draw bond			H—O—H	O—C—O
add lone pairs	none required for hydrogen			
check octet	ok	ok	ok	C is not 8e
molecular drawing				

4.8 Learning Check   Draw Proper Lewis structures for each of the following species that obey the octet rule.

PH_3, $CHCl_3$, NH_4^+, H_2CO, SeF_2, PCl_4^+

VSEPR Theory and Molecular Shapes I

Valence Shell Electron Pair Repulsion theory says that the pairs of electrons around the central atom will repel each other and therefore move to an orientation to minimize the repulsion (the lowest potential energy).

Lone pairs are attracted to only one nucleus, and therefore will be short and fat, while bonding pairs are attracted to two nuclei will be drawn out. The net result is that lone pair / lone pair repulsion is greatest, while bonding pair/ bonding pair repulsion is least. This means that the presence of lone pairs can disrupt the equal distribution of the lone pairs around the central atom.

Total e- pairs on central atom	electron distribution	Bond Pairs	Lone Pairs	Shape (atoms only, not lone pairs)	Bond Angle	Molecular Shape Example
2	Linear	2	0	Linear	180°	
3	Planar Triangle	3	0	Planar Triangle	120°	
4	Tetrahedral	4	0	Tetrahedral	109.5°	
		3	1	Trigonal Pyramid	107°	
		2	2	Bent/ V-Shape	104.5°	

You must distinguish between the distribution of the electrons around the central atom and the molecular shape which only takes the atoms into account - not the lone pairs.

The presence of a double bond in the Lewis structure does not affect the shape. Special Note

You need to only count the number of lone pairs and atoms surrounding the central atom.

Name the shape in each case of Learning Check 4.8 4.9 Learning Check

Bond Polarity and Molecular Polarity

A bond is polar when there is a difference in electronegativity between the two atoms bonded.

The more electronegative atom has a partial negative charge "∂⁻", while the less electronegative atom has a partial positive charge, "∂⁺".

A molecule will be polar if there is an overall polarity difference when you consider all the bonds, and their orientation in a molecule.

If the dipole moments (like vectors) cancel out, then there will be no net dipole and the molecule will be non-polar.

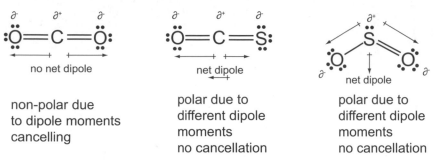

non-polar due to dipole moments cancelling

polar due to different dipole moments no cancellation

polar due to different dipole moments no cancellation

Figure 4.5: Dipole moments and molecular polarity

Property	Polar Molecule	Non-Polar Molecule	
ΔE-neg	Significant difference in electronegativity		zero or very low difference in electro-negativity
bond type	polar bonds	polar bonds	non-polar bonds
symmetry	non-symmetrical	symmetrical	doesn't matter
result	net dipole	dipoles cancel, no net dipole	no dipoles

Bond Length and Strength

As the number of shared electrons increase, the attractive force increases, so the bond strength (bond energy / bond enthalpy) increases. As the force of attraction increases, the bond length decreases.

bond	Number of bonds	Bond Length (pm)	Bond Strength (kJ/mol)
C–C	1	0.154	348
C=C	2	0.134	612
C≡C	3	0.120	837

Be careful – the double bond is not doubly strong.

Allotropes of Carbon – Graphite, Diamond & Fullerene

| Allotropes are different molecular or crystalline structures of an element |

Definition

Carbon exists as three different allotropes:

	Diamond	Graphite	Fullerene
Conductivity	None – all electrons are used in bonding	High – only 3 electrons used in bonding – the fourth electron is able to move throughout the sheet	Intermediate – surface of the "ball" is conductive, but imagine an ant running across the surface of a lot of basketballs
Geometry	3-dimensional	2-dimensional	2 dimensional folded into a sphere
Hardness	Very hard – all atoms are held together in the lattice by strong covalent bonds	Very soft – 2 dimension sheets slide over each other because of weak van der Waals' forces between the sheets	Soft – imagine the molecular form of the "ball room at McDonald's"

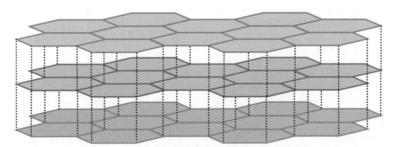

Figure 4.6: Three layers of Graphite

In Figure 4.6 each coloured sheet is attracted to the others by weak van der Waals' forces - shown by the dotted lines. The electrical conductivity occurs along a single sheet due to the non-bonding electron.

Many students get confused between the two properties...

Property	Explanation
Conductivity	Each carbon in graphite is bonded to 3 others, therefore there is an extra electron which is able to move across the entire sheet.
soft powder	Because each sheet is non-polar, the sheets have only van der Waals' forces acting between them, therefore they slide over each other very easily

Intermolecular Forces

Intermolecular forces are the forces that attract one molecule to another molecule. These are the forces that govern physical properties – melting & boiling points, density, volatility etc. There are three inter<u>molecular</u> forces.

Van der Waals' Forces or London Dispersion Forces

Van der Waals' forces are the result of a temporary, instantaneous or momentary dipole inducing a dipole in a nearby particle and the resulting attraction between the two temporary dipoles.

Because the attractive force is only temporary, van der Waals' forces are the weakest of all.

even electron distribution   "A" undergoes momentary polarization

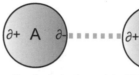

a dipole is induced in "B", and the two
temporary dipoles are attracted to each other

Dipole – Dipole Forces

This is perhaps the most common intermolecular force. It occurs between all polar molecules, which have permanent dipoles.
Because the dipole is now permanent the forces are stronger.

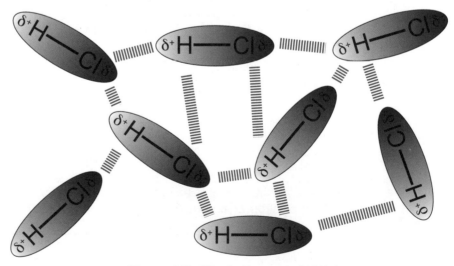

Figure 4.7: Dipole Forces in HCl(g)

Hydrogen Bonding

There are only three structures that lead to hydrogen bonding. A hydrogen atom must be attached **directly** to a fluorine, oxygen or nitrogen (Hydrogen bonding is "FON" – like fun)

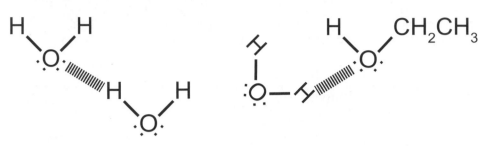

Figure 4.8: Hydrogen bonding between water and ethanol molecules

Ethers ($R-CH_2-O-CH_2-R$), aldehydes($R-CHO$), ketones($RCOR'$), and esters($R-COO-R'$) do not have hydrogen bonding, because the H atom is not attached directly to an O atom. See Organic Chemistry for structures.

Exam Trap

In some cases, hydrogen bonding gives rise to molecules "pairing up" to become dimers. The reciprocal hydrogen bonding in ethanoic acid is an example.

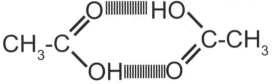

Figure 4.9: Hydrogen bonded dimer of ethanoic acid

Often we are concerned with the intermolecular forces that exists within a pure substance. We should also consider how a substance interacts in a mixture.
Propanone, without a O-H group, cannot hydrogen bond with itself, it can only use it's dipole-dipole forces. So the boiling point of propanone is 56.5°C.

However, water can hydrogen bond to propanone's lone pairs on the oxygen. So propanone is soluble in water.

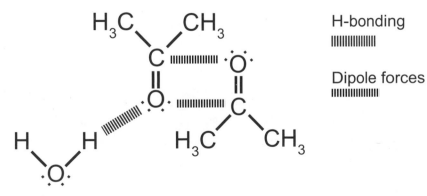

H-bonding

Dipole forces

Figure 4.10: Propanone hydrogen bonding with water and the weak dipole-dipole forces between propanone molecules

The layering of intermolecular forces

It is common to speak of the strongest type of intermolecular force present. You must remember, however, that all of the weaker forces exist as well.

	H_2O	CH_3Cl	CH_4
strong	Hydrogen bond		
medium	dipole/dipole	dipole/dipole	
weak	van der Waals'	van der Waals'	van der Waals'

Table 4.11: The layering of Intermolecular forces

How do you determine the type of IMF?

Is there a H atom attached directly to F, O or N? If "Yes" = Hydrogen bonding
Is the molecule non-polar (low Δ E-neg or symmetrical)? = Yes = Van der Waals' / London Forces
All others are dipole – dipole.

Van der Waals'	Hydrogen bonding	Dipole – Dipole
Non-polar molecules e.g.... Any molecular element like Cl_2, Br_2, O_2, P_4, S_8 etc. and hydrocarbons CH_4 etc	H–F (only one molecule!) H–O– (alcohols, carboxylic acids, water) H–N< (amines, amides, ammonia)	Any other molecule that is not covered by the previous two. A covalent molecule that has different non-metals, not symmetrically oriented.

Table 4.12: Types of Intermolecular Forces

Types of Solids

In all types of bonding, we can consider a solid as a lattice of particles. The type of bonding depends on the type of particle and the forces that exist between them.

Ionic (compounds only)

The attractive force between oppositely charged ions. The lattice is made of oppositely charged ions. Salts are ionic. SALTS ARE NOT MOLECULES.

Covalent – Giant (elements or compounds)

Regular old covalent bonds, but they exist between ALL atoms – that is every atom is covalently bonded to all of its nearest neighbours. The lattice is made of atoms covalently bonded to each other.

Covalent – Molecular (elements or compounds)

Regular covalent bonds, but the atoms form little packages called molecules. Each package is held together by strong bonds, but they are attracted to each other by weak forces – see IMF below.

Metallic (elements only)

Metallic bonding is the electrostatic attraction between a lattice of positive ions and delocalized electrons

Physical Properties and Intermolecular Forces

The strength of the intermolecular forces govern physical properties. It takes energy to overcome these forces of attraction in order to melt or boil the compound.
We are not breaking the covalent bond here, just separating molecules from each other.

Bonding	Lattice Forces	boiling point	volatility	ΔH_{vap}
ionic	Ionic	high	low	high
metallic	ion / electron	high	low	high
giant covalent	covalent	high	low	high
molecular covalent	Hydrogen bonding Dipole / Dipole van der Waals'	low	high	low

Volatility is a measure of the tendency for a substance to evaporate.   Definition

ΔH_{vap} *is the potential energy change required to vaporize a liquid.*   Definition

Summary Questions

1. Write the names of the following compounds...
   a) $Ca(NO_3)_2$
   b) $Cu(NO_3)_2$
   c) $Al_2(SO_4)_3$
   d) $Fe_3(PO_4)_2$
   e) NH_4Cl
   f) $NaHCO_3$

2. Determine the correct formula of the following compounds
   a) potassium oxide
   b) ammonium nitrate
   c) magnesium carbonate
   d) nickel(III) oxide
   e) lead(IV) oxide
   f) aluminium phosphate

3. Draw a correct Lewis structure for the following covalent compounds...
   a) CO
   b) NI_3
   c) CH_2Cl_2
   d) NO_2^-
   e) NO_2^+

4. Determine the dominant intermolecular force in the following molecules...
   a) CH_3OH
   b) CH_2Cl_2
   c) CH_3OCH_3
   d) CH_3CHO
   e) CH_3COOH
   f) CH_3COCH_3

5. State and explain which of the BCl_3 and NCl_3 has a higher melting point

CHAPTER 5

ENERGETICS

Endothermic & Exothermic

The first law of thermodynamics (Energetics) says that energy cannot be created nor destroyed; it can only change forms.

We divide the universe into two parts – the system and the surroundings. Most people have a basic understanding of what these two are, but there are some important details.

As far as Chemists are concerned, the system is represented by the potential energy of the bonds, and the surroundings are represented by the kinetic energy of particles. We cannot measure the potential energy directly in the lab, so we must react chemicals together and measure the change of the kinetic energy of the surroundings – and assume that they are equal (i.e. no energy escaped our measurement)

So if we consider two chemicals reacting in aqueous solution – say an acid and a base reacting exothermically. The system made up of the acid (H^+ ions), the base (OH^- ions) and the water product (H_2O). The separate ions have a higher potential energy than the product, so the energy flows into the surroundings as heat, and we see the temperature of the surroundings increase.

If thermal energy is flowing into the system, then the surroundings are losing energy, and the system is gaining energy

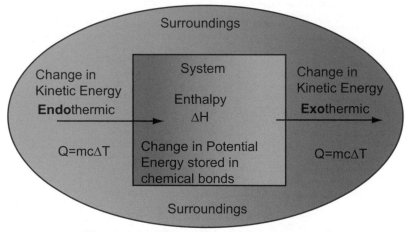

Figure 5.1: Energy flow in "The Universe"

Many students make the mistake of thinking that the solvent in an aqueous reaction is part of the system - but is it? - NO - the water that ions or molecules are dissolved in is not involved in the chemical changes. The solvent is part of the surroundings.

You need to think about the flow of energy (heat) between the system and the surroundings. If one gains, then the other loses. What form does the energy take in the different parts of "the universe"?

Property	Endothermic	Exothermic
System	Gains potential energy	Loses potential energy
Surroundings	Loses kinetic energy	Gains kinetic energy
Enthalpy change (ΔH)	Positive ($\Delta H > 0$)	Negative ($\Delta H < 0$)
Temperature change (ΔT)	Negative ($\Delta T < 0$)	Positive ($\Delta T > 0$)
Bonding	Bond Breaking	Bond Making

Table 5.2: Endothermic vs. Exothermic

As chemists, we are interested in the system - the chemical bonds. However we are forced to use changes in the surroundings to infer what happens in the system.

Potential Energy Diagrams (Enthalpy Diagrams)

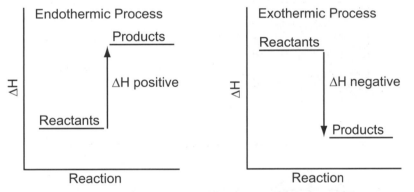

Figure 5.3: Potential Energy Diagrams / Enthalpy Diagrams

In the endothermic graph on the left, the system gains potential energy as the reactants become products. The value for ΔH is greater than zero.
In the exothermic graph on the right, the system loses potential energy to the surroundings as the reaction proceeds. The enthalpy change is negative.

In terms of stability, do not say that something is "unstable". Stability is relative. In Figure 5.3, the endothermic process has reactants which are more stable than products. In the exothermic process, the products are more stable.

Calorimetry - Enthalpy Change Calculations

In order to calculate a change in the potential energy of the system, we must measure the equal but opposite energy change in the surroundings. The energy change of the surroundings is given by

$$Q = mc\Delta T,$$

Where Q is the Quantity of energy in Joules
m is the mass of the material changing temperature
c is the specific heat capacity of the substance changing temperature
ΔT is the change in temperature $(T_2 - T_1)$

Be Careful!   Physics students will be familiar with c_{H_2O} being 4200 $J \cdot kg^{-1\circ} \cdot C^{-1}$ – because physicists like kilograms
Chemists tend to prefer grams, but you shouldn't be thrown here.

Exam Trap   Usually you have two masses – the mass of the material changing temperature, and the mass of the reactants (fuel) causing the change. – Don't get them mixed up.

Because energy cannot be created or destroyed,

$$E_{lost} = -E_{gained}$$

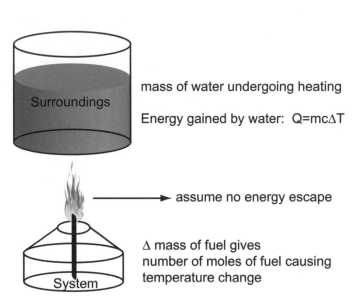

mass of water undergoing heating

Energy gained by water: $Q = mc\Delta T$

assume no energy escape

Δ mass of fuel gives number of moles of fuel causing temperature change

Figure 5.4: Determining the Enthalpy Change of a Fuel

As chemists we are interested in the energy change per amount of substance (moles) causing the change.

$$\Delta H = \frac{-Q}{1000 \cdot n}$$

Expression

Where ΔH is the enthalpy change of the system in $kJ \cdot mol^{-1}$,
Q is the energy change of the surroundings in J
n is the number of moles of **limiting** reactant.
we need to divide by 1000 to convert Joules to kilojoules.

However, there are many cases where you aren't burning a fuel and capturing the heat. Often times you are mixing reactants. How will the change of volume or concentration affect the temperature change?

Mixing 50 cm³ of 0.1 M HCl and 50 cm³ of 0.1 M NaOH causes a temperature change of ΔT.   Classic Question

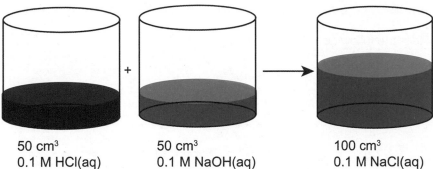

50 cm³   50 cm³   100 cm³
0.1 M HCl(aq)   0.1 M NaOH(aq)   0.1 M NaCl(aq)

a) *How does mixing 100 cm³ of each solution affect ΔT?*

b) *How does mixing 100 cm³ of HCl(aq) with 50 cm³ of NaOH affect ΔT?*

c) *How does mixing 50 cm³ of 0.2 M solutions affect ΔT?*

Answers
a) No Change! – yes you have doubled the heat, but it has to affect double the mass, so the two doublings cancel out.
b) Don't forget stoichiometry! – NaOH is still the Limiting reactant – therefore no change in the amount of heat produced, but it has to cause a temperature change for a larger mass, so the change in temperature is actually less!
c) Temperature change doubles. Doubling the number of moles without changing the mass is the only way to double the ΔT!

Hess' Law

Enthalpy is what is known as a "state function", which means that it depends only upon the initial and final states, not the pathway between the states – the pathway is what is of concern in kinetics.

There are many ways to solve these problems. The simplest and most familiar way to solve these problems is to treat them as a system of equations.

You are always given equations to manipulate and a equation which is the goal.

Consider the following example.

Classic Question

Determine the enthalpy of reaction for

$$NO(g) + \tfrac{1}{2}O_2(g) \rightarrow NO_2(g)$$

given

① $\tfrac{1}{2}N_2(g) + O_2(g) \rightarrow NO_2(g)$ $\Delta H = + 33.8\ kJ$

② $\tfrac{1}{2}N_2(g) + \tfrac{1}{2}O_2(g) \rightarrow NO(g)$ $\Delta H = -113.14\ kJ$

Looking at equation ① we see our desired product, $NO_2(g)$ in the correct position, however in equation ②, the reactant NO is on the wrong side, so we will reverse the entire equation and change the sign of the enthalpy change to positive.

① $\tfrac{1}{2}N_2(g) + O_2(g) \rightarrow NO_2(g)$ $\Delta H = + 33.8\ kJ$

(-)② $NO(g) \rightarrow \tfrac{1}{2}N_2(g) + \tfrac{1}{2}O_2(g)$ $\Delta H = +113.14\ kJ$

This also allows us to cancel out the $N_2(g)$, which is not desired in our final equation. The oxygen cancels out to leave a half on the left side. Adding up the two equations, and the values for ΔH we get...

$$NO(g) + \tfrac{1}{2}O_2(g) \rightarrow NO_2(g) \qquad \Delta H = + 146.94\ kJ$$

Remember, what ever you do to the equations, you do to the value of the enthalpy. It will and must work out to the final answer.

You will usually either flip the equation or double it or both.

Now try the following...

5.1 Learning Check

1. *Determine the heat of reaction for ...*

$$BaO(s) + H_2SO_4(l) \rightarrow BaSO_4(s) + H_2O(l)$$

given

$BaO(s) + SO_3(g) \rightarrow BaSO_4$ $\Delta H = -213.0\ kJ$

$SO_3(g) + H_2O \rightarrow H_2SO_4(l)$ $\Delta H = -78.2\ kJ$

2. Determine the enthalpy for the following reaction
   $$2NO(g) + O_2(g) \rightarrow N_2O_4(g)$$
   given that

$N_2O_4(g) \rightarrow 2NO_2(g)$	$\Delta H = + 57.93 \ kJ$
$NO(g) + \frac{1}{2}O_2(g) \rightarrow NO_2(g)$	$\Delta H = - 56.57 \ kJ$

3. Hydrogen peroxide decomposes by the reaction...
   $$H_2O_2(l) \rightarrow H_2O(l) + \frac{1}{2}O_2(g)$$

   Determine the enthalpy of decomposition by manipulating the following equations.

$H_2(g) + O_2(g) \rightarrow H_2O_2(l)$	$\Delta H = -188 \ kJ$
$H_2(g) + \frac{1}{2}O_2 \rightarrow H_2O(l)$	$\Delta H = -286 \ kJ$

4. Given the following data:

$S(s) + \frac{3}{2}O_2(g) \rightarrow SO_3(g)$	$\Delta H = -395.2 \ kJ$
$2SO_2(g) + O_2(g) \rightarrow 2SO_3(g)$	$\Delta H = -198.2 \ kJ$

   Calculate the ΔH of the reaction...
   $$S(s) + O_2(g) \rightarrow SO_2(g)$$

5. Given the following data:

$C_2H_2(g) + \frac{5}{2}O_2(g) \rightarrow 2CO_2(g) + H_2O(l)$	$\Delta H = -1300 \ kJ$
$C(s) + O_2(g) \rightarrow CO_2(g)$	$\Delta H = -394 \ kJ$
$H_2(g) + \frac{1}{2}O_2(g) \rightarrow H_2O(l)$	$\Delta H = -286 \ kJ$

   Calculate ΔH for the reaction...
   $$2C(s) + H_2(g) \rightarrow C_2H_2(g)$$

Bond Enthalpy

Definition

> *Bond enthalpy is the energy required to break one mole of a certain type of bond in the gaseous state averaged across a variety of compounds.*

This means that, for example, there are lots of compounds with a C-H bond, so many different compounds are used to determine the C-H bond strength, and the average is then calculate. - So, no single compound has the same value of C-H bond strength. It is often slightly different from the experimentally determined values.

There are values given in the data book for bond enthalpy, but how do you use them? What's the formula? Consider Figure 5.3. We want to move from reactants to products (light blue), but have to go via atoms. We need to break the reactants (red arrow), and then make the products (green).

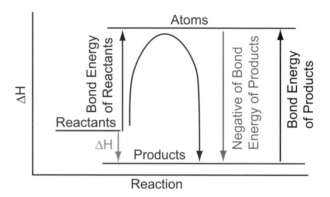

Figure 5.5: Bond Enthalpy Potential Energy diagram

Because we are taking the opposite value of the bond enthalpy of the products the mathematical formula becomes...

$$\Delta H = \sum B.E._{(reactants)} - \sum B.E._{(products)}$$

Example

Let's use the Haber process as a classic example.

$$N_2(g) + H_2(g) \rightleftharpoons 2NH_3(g)$$

You have to draw the molecules out to get a better feel for what you are dealing with. Draw the Lewis structures in the space here.

Strength of the reactant bonds	Strength of the product bonds
(N≡N) + 3(H-H)	6(N-H)
(944 kJ) + 3(436 kJ)	6(388 kJ)
2252 kJ	2328 kJ

So it takes more energy to break the products. From this we know that the products are more stable, and therefore should be at a lower potential energy (enthalpy) than the products. This means the reaction is exothermic and the value should be negative.

$$\Delta H = \sum B.E._{(reactants)} - \sum B.E._{(products)}$$
$$\Delta H = 2252 \text{ kJ} - 2328 \text{ kJ}$$
$$\Delta H = -74 \text{ kJ} \text{ (exothermic as predicted)}$$

Determine the enthalpy of reaction for the following reactions. Be sure to draw out the correct Lewis structure of the molecules so that you identify the correct number and type of bonds. Use your data book.

5.2 Learning
Check

1. $CH_4 + 2O_2(g) \rightarrow CO_2 + 2H_2O$

2. $H_2C=CH_2(g) + Br_2 \rightarrow H_2BrC-CBrH_2$

3. $H_2N-NH_2 + O_2 \rightarrow N_2 + 2H_2O$

4. $H_2 + Cl_2 \rightarrow 2HCl$

5. $CH_3COOH + 2O_2 \rightarrow 2CO_2 + 2H_2O$

Summary Questions

1. Determine the heat evolved in the reaction
   $Al_2O_3(s) + 6Na(s) \rightarrow 2Al(s) + 3Na_2O(s)$

   Given
   $2Al(s) + \frac{3}{2}O_2(g) \rightarrow Al_2O_3(s)$ $\Delta H = -1590 \ kJ \ mol^{-1}$
   $2Na(s) + \frac{1}{2}O_2(g) \rightarrow Na_2O(s)$ $\Delta H = -422.6 \ kJ \ mol^{-1}$

2. When 250 cm^3 of 0.500 M KOH(aq) and 250cm^3 of 0.500 HCl(aq) are mixed in a insulated styrofoam container, the temperature rises from 24.6°C to 28.0°C. Determine the enthalpy of reaction.

3. How will the temperature change in Question 2 change when...
   a) both volumes are doubled?
   b) both concentrations are doubled?
   c) the concentration of acid is doubled?
   d) the volume of acid is doubled?

Chapter 6

Kinetics

Rates of Reaction

Definition

$$\text{Rate of reaction} = \frac{\Delta[\text{Reactants}]}{\Delta\text{time}} = \frac{\Delta[\text{Products}]}{\Delta\text{time}}$$

Rate of reaction are "officially" measured in the change of concentration per second (mol•dm^{-3}•s^{-1}), but there are other units that are used practically.
In experiments, we don't have a way of measuring concentration directly so we have to convert from other measurements.

Rate Experiments

- Rate of gas production – collection of gas (with a syringe)
- Rate of gas production – loss of mass of reactants
- Rate of change of concentration – absorption of light
- Rate of increase in precipitate formation (cloudiness of reaction mixture) – blocking of light
- Time to consume a reactant (simple) – e.g. time for Mg strip to react and dissolve in acid
- Time to consume a reactant (clock reaction) – I_2 clock

In all the above types of measurements, we must use the limiting reactant to determine the rate.

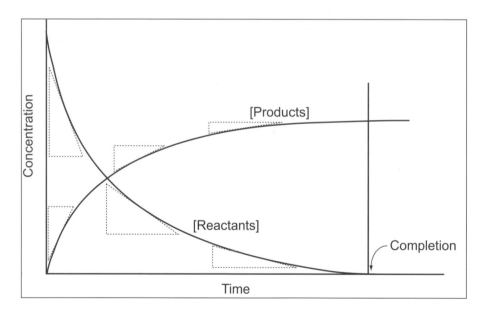

Figure 6.1: Reaction going to completion

As rate is the change of concentration over time, this is seen as the slope of the tangents in Figures 6.1 and 6.2.
If the graph of the reactants goes to zero the reaction has gone to completion. If the graph of the reactants levels out at some positive value, (i.e. there are still reactants remaining) then the reaction has reached equilibrium.
As you can see, the rate changes over time, so chemists of speak of the "initial rate", before reactant concentration can change.

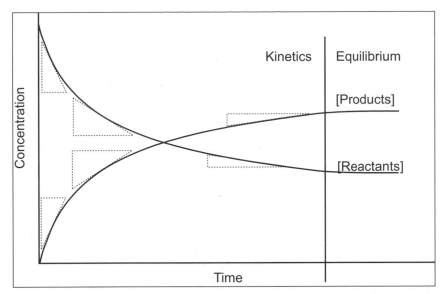

Figure 6.2: Reaction achieving equilibrium

Collision Theory

In order for a chemical reaction to occur the particles must...   Theory
*   Collide
*   in the right orientation
*   with sufficient energy (more than the activation energy barrier)

Factors affecting Rate of Reaction

There are four factors which affect the rate of reaction. Each needs to be explained in terms of one or more of the points in the collision theory.
1.   Concentration / Pressure
2.   Surface Area
3.   Temperature
4.   Catalyst

Lets take each one in turn.

1. Concentration / Pressure.

The concentration of a solution or the pressure of a gas is simply the number of particles per unit volume. In a concentrated solution, the particles are packed closer together so the number of collisions per unit time will increase.

2. Surface Area

Collisions can only occur on the surface of a solid. If you cut a potato in half, then the boiling water can reach the "inside" surface that it couldn't previously. So the number of collisions per time increases.

3. Temperature

As noted earlier, temperature is a measure of the kinetic energy of the particles. If the particles have more kinetic energy, then there will be an increase in the frequency of collisions. But that's not the whole explanation. Because the particles have more energy, there are a greater number of particles with sufficient energy to overcome the energy barrier represented by the Activation Energy. This is demonstrated by two temperature curves of the "Maxwell-Boltzman Energy Distribution"

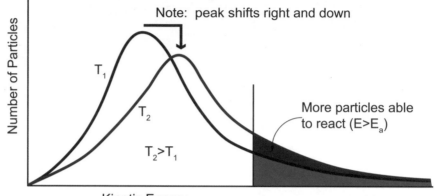

Figure 6.3: Maxwell-Boltzman Distribution at two different temperatures

In Figure 6.3, the blue area represents the amount (moles) of particles that have energy greater than the activation energy, and therefore are able to react.

When the sample is heated to a higher temperature, the average energy of the particles increases, and the curve shifts to the right. The red area represents the increased number of particles that have sufficient energy to react at the higher temperature.

The entire area under one of the curves represents the total number of particles in the sample.

You do not give the particles activation energy. Activation energy is the energy barrier.

Note that the peak of the curve shifts to the right and downwards.

Exam Hint

You need to be able to draw and explain this graph if asked about temperature effects.

4. Catalyst.

> *A catalyst speeds up a chemical reaction by providing an alternate pathway that has a lower activation energy.*
>
> *Catalysts are not consumed in a chemical reaction.*

Definition

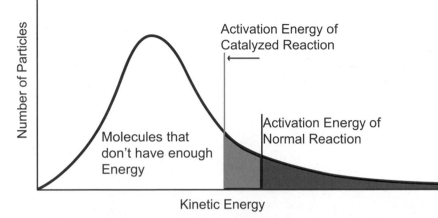

Figure 6.4: Maxwell Boltzmann distribution for a normal and a catalysed reaction

As in the definition, a catalyst lowers the activation energy so therefore there are a greater number of particles able to react at a given temperature.

In the case of catalysts and temperature, there are more particles that have enough energy to react.

CHAPTER 7

EQUILIBRIUM

Dynamic Equilibrium

Equilibrium is related to rates of reaction.

Definition

> **Equilibrium** is achieved when the forward rate of reaction and the reverse **rates of reaction are equal**.

Dynamic equilbrium exists in a closed system when there is no change in the macroscopic properties (i.e. concentrations).

Approaching equilibrium

Before two reactants are mixed the concentration of the products is zero.

As the two reactants mix, they react to form products, and the concentration of products increases.

As [product] increases, the rate of the reverse reaction must also increase (rate $\propto$ [product]). At some point in time, as more products are formed from the forward reaction, they have sufficient concentration to cause the reverse rate of reaction to be equal to the rate of the forward reaction.

It doesn't matter which direction you approach equilibrium from, at some point the two rates will equal.

Position of Equilibrium

As chemists, we are interested in the products of our reactions, not the reactants. So we want to know how the amount of products compares to the amount of reactants. This is the idea behind the equilibrium constant.

$$K_c = \frac{[Products]}{[Reactants]}$$

Lucky for us it is easy to write the equilibrium expression for any balanced equation

Consider the generic reaction $aA + bB \rightleftharpoons dD + eE$

$$K_c = \frac{[D]^d[E]^e}{[A]^a[B]^b}$$

(the concentration of each species is raised to the power of its coefficient)

Classic examples

Haber Process $N_2(g) + 3H_2(g) \rightleftharpoons 2NH_3(g)$

$$K_c = \frac{[NH_3]^2}{[N_2][H_2]^3}$$

Contact Process $2SO_2(g) + O_2(g) \rightleftharpoons 2SO_3(g)$

$$K_c = \frac{[SO_3]^2}{[SO_2]^2[O_2]}$$

Write the equilibrium expression for each of the following reactions.

1. $2H_2S(g) + 3O_2(g) \rightleftharpoons 2H_2O(g) + 2SO_2(g)$
2. $2N_2O_5(g) \rightleftharpoons 4NO_2(g) + O_2(g)$
3. $CO(g) + 2H_2(g) \rightleftharpoons CH_3OH(g)$
4. $4NH_3(g) + 3O_2(g) \rightleftharpoons 2N_2(g) + 6H_2O(g)$
5. $2N_2O(g) + 3O_2(g) \rightleftharpoons 4NO_2(g)$

7.1 Learning Check

LeChâtelier's Principle

When an equilibrium system is stressed, the system will shift the position equilibrium so as to remove the stress.

Definition

Many candidates lose points here, not because they don't understand, but because they are not thorough enough with their answers.

A classic example with degrees of answer quality…

"State and explain the effect of increasing pressure on the amount of product in the Haber Process, $N_2(g) + 3H_2(g) \rightleftharpoons 2NH_3(g)$"

Classic Question

1. It shifts right.
2. It increases the product.
3. It increases product by shifting right.
4. It increases the amount of NH_3 by shifting to the right.
5. It increases the amount of NH_3 by shifting the equilibrium to the right to remove the stress.
6. It increases the amount of NH_3 by shifting the equilibrium to the right to remove the stress because there are fewer moles of gas of products than of reactants.
7. An increase in pressure shifts the equilibrium to the right because as four moles of reactant gases become two moles of product gas, the pressure is returned to its original state.
8. There is an increase in the amount of product because an increase in pressure shifts the equilibrium to the right, as four moles of gaseous reactant become two moles of gaseous product the pressure is reduced.

Model Answer

Stress	Result
Increasing concentration	Shift away from the species being increased in order to lower the concentration.
Removal of a species	Shift towards that species in order to maintain its concentration. This is usually accomplished by adding something else that reacts with only that species. E.g. the addition of base will consume any H^+ ions, and vice versa. E.g. The addition of $Ag^+(aq)$ ions will precipitate any halide ions, $Cl^-(aq)$
Increasing pressure by decreasing volume	Shift towards the side with fewer moles **of gas**.
Adding a catalyst	No effect as it increases the rate of the forward and reverse reaction equally.
Adding an inert gas (increase pressure)	No effect (because it does not increase the partial pressure of a reactant or product).
Increasing Temperature	**Affects the equilibrium constant** - see below. Favours the endothermic reaction.

Changes in pressure or concentration only force the equilibrium to shift left or right in order to restore the equality of the rates of reaction and maintain the equilibrium constant.

Be Careful

However, a change in temperature actually changes the value of K_c.

K_c is dependant upon temperature. As temperature increases, the rate of the exothermic reaction direction increases. This will change the relative concentrations of reactants and products.

Often you are given information about the nature of the reactants and products and asked to answer the question based on that information

Example

In the reaction $2NO_2(g) \rightleftharpoons N_2O_4(g)$, NO_2 is a orange/brown gas, and N_2O_4 is colourless.

State and explain the effect of increasing pressure on the colour of the gases in the container.

Answer
As the pressure is increased, the equilibrium will shift to the products (right) because there is only one mole of gas of product compared to two moles of reactant. Shifting to the right will lower the pressure. Therefore the colour will fade.

The meaning of K_c

As chemists, we are interested in the products of our reactions, so in terms of K_c, we are interested in increasing the value of K_c, and thus increasing the extent of the reaction.

$K_c >>> 1$	Reaction goes to completion
$K_c > 1$	Equilibrium position favours products
$K_c \approx 1$	Reactant and product concentrations similar
$K_c < 1$	Equilibrium position favours reactants

The Haber Process

The Haber process is how ammonia is produced from its elements.

$$N_2(g) + 3H_2(g) \rightleftharpoons 2NH_3 \qquad \Delta H < 0$$

How can the amount of ammonia be maximized?

Looking at the equation, we want a high pressure so that the equilbrium is driven to the right side as 4 moles of reactant gases become 2 moles of produce gas.

Because the reaction is exothermic, we should run this reaction at a low temperature, however this causes a problem. Rate depends upon temperature. Low temperature means low rate. How can we increase the rate with out increasing the temperature? Answer: use a catalyst!. Iron metal is the catalyst used in the Haber process.

Factor	Value	Comment
Pressure	200 atm	The cost of builiding high pressure containers is a limiting factor
Temperature	400°C	Not too hot(equilbrium), but not too cold (rate)
Catalyst	Fe	Used to have a fast rate at a low temperature

Summary Questions

1. Balance the following equations and write the equilibrium constant for the reaction

   a) $N_2O_4(g) \rightleftharpoons NO_2(g)$
   b) $SiH_4(g) + Cl_2(g) \rightleftharpoons SiCl_4(g) + H_2(g)$
   c) $PBr_3(g) + Cl_2(g) \rightleftharpoons PCl_3(g) + Br_2(g)$
   d) $CO(g) + H_2(g) \rightleftharpoons CH_3OH(g)$
   e) $NO_2(g) \rightleftharpoons NO(g) + O_2(g)$

2. Nitric oxide reacts with oxygen exothemically to produce NO_2, which is a dark brown gas.

   $$2NO(g) + O_2(g) \rightleftharpoons 2NO_2(g)$$

   How will the colour of the mixture change if...
   a) pressure is increased by reducing the volume of the container?
   b) temperature is increased?
   c) a catalyst is added?
   d) neon gas is added to increase the pressure?
   e) more oxygen is added?

CHAPTER 8

ACIDS & BASES

IN THIS CHAPTER...

Brønsted-Lowry Definition of Acids and Bases

Definition

> *An acid is a substance that can donate protons, $H^+(aq)$ ions. A base is a substance that can accept protons, $H^+(aq)$ ions.*

An acid is any substance, that when mixed with water forms H^+ ions. Bases used to be regarded as only those compounds which contain OH^- ions, but ammonia is a base - how does that work?

$$NH_3(aq) + H_2O(l) \rightleftharpoons NH_4^+(aq) + OH^-(aq)$$

NH_3 can accept a proton from water to form . The presence of OH^- makes the resulting solution alkaline.

Properties of Acids & Bases

There are five types of reactions that acids undergo. They are based on the five different types of base. In most cases, a base can be defined as anything that reacts with an acid. Bases often contain metals. The five reactions can be organized into three groups as follows...

Acids react with reactive metals to produce hydrogen gas and a salt.
$$2HCl(aq) + Mg(s) \rightarrow MgCl_2(aq) + H_2(g)$$

Acids react with oxides and hydroxides to produce water and a salt
$$2HCl(aq) + MgO(s) \rightarrow MgCl_2(aq) + H_2O(l)$$
$$2HCl(aq) + Mg(OH)_2(s) \rightarrow MgCl_2(aq) + 2H_2O(l)$$

Acids react with carbonates and hydrogen carbonates to produce carbon dioxide, water and salt.
$$2HCl(aq) + MgCO_3(s) \rightarrow MgCl_2(aq) + H_2O(l) + CO_2(g)$$
$$2HCl(aq) + Mg(HCO_3)_2(s) \rightarrow MgCl_2(aq) + 2H_2O(l) + 2CO_2(g)$$

Alkalis are soluble bases. So all alkalis are bases, but not all bases are alkali.

8.1 Learning Check

Complete and balance the following equations

$HNO_3(aq) + NaHCO_3(aq) \rightarrow$
$Al_2O_3(s) + HCl(aq) \rightarrow$
$ZnO(s) + H_2SO_4(aq) \rightarrow$
$Mg(s) + HNO_3(aq) \rightarrow$
$H_2SO_4(aq) + CuCO_3(s) \rightarrow$
$HCl(aq) + Ca(OH)_2(aq) \rightarrow$

$H^+(aq)$ or $H_3O^+(aq)$?

Either notation is fine. Strictly speaking, $H_3O^+(aq)$ - the "hydronium ion" is more correct. This text will use $H^+(aq)$ for convenience.

Conjugate pairs

Definition

> A conjugate pair are two species differing by a single proton, H^+

$HCl \rightarrow H+(aq) + Cl^-(aq)$ the Cl^- ion is the conjugate base of HCl
$NH_3(aq) + H^+(aq) \rightarrow NH_4^+(aq)$ the NH_4^+ ion is the conjugate acid of NH_3

1. Write the conjugate acid for the following bases

8.2 Learning
Check

   a) F^- b) N_2H_4 c) C_5H_5N

   d) O_2^{2-} e) $HCrO_4^-$ f) HO_2^-

2. Write the conjugate base for the following acids

   a) NH_3 b) HCO_3^- c) HCN

   d) H_5IO_6 e) HNO_3 f) H_2O

3. Identify the conjugate pairs in the following equations

   a) $HNO_3 + N_2H_4 \rightleftharpoons NO_3^- + N_2H_5^+$
      Acid   base   conj. base   conj acid

   b) $NH_3 + N_2H_5^+ \rightleftharpoons NH_4^+ + N_2H_4$
      base   acid   conj acid   conj base

   c) $H_2PO_4^- + CO_3^{2-} \rightleftharpoons HPO_4^{2-} + HCO_3^-$
      Acid   base   conj base   conj acid

   d) $HIO_3 + HC_2O_4^- \rightleftharpoons IO_3^- + H_2C_2O_4$

Amphoterism

Definition

> An amphoteric substance is one that may behave as either an acid or a base.

How do you know? – You look at the other species that it is reacting with. If it reacting with an known acid, then the amphoteric substance is behaving like a base, and vice versa.

This is a good place for IB examiners to combine questions – usually conjugates go well with amphoteric species.
This is an opportunity for you to apply the definitions of acids and bases.

$H_2CO_3(aq) \rightleftharpoons$ | $HCO_3^-(aq)$ + | $H^+(aq) \rightleftharpoons$ $CO_3^{2-}(aq)$ + $2H^+(aq)$
acid--------- | conjugate base
         | acid-------   --------------   conjugate base

so $HCO_3^-(aq)$ can act as a base or an acid – it's amphoteric.

Strong & Weak

Electrolytes are any substance that dissolves in water to produce ions (and hence conduct electricity). Electrolytes may be acids, bases or salts.

Definition

> *A strong electrolyte dissociates completely into ions - ionizes 100%*
>
> *A weak electrolyte does not completely dissociate into ions- only partially dissociates*

The IB syllabus indicates the following as strong and weak acids and bases you should know.

	Acids	Bases
Strong	HCl - hydrochloric acid HNO_3 - nitric acid H_2SO_4 - sulphuric acid	LiOH, NaOH, KOH $Ba(OH)_2$
Weak	CH_3COOH – ethanoic acid H_2CO_3 – carbonic acid– only (aq)	NH_3 – ammonia CH_3NH_2 – ethanamine

Table 8.1: IB Syllabus Acids & Bases - Memorize them!

Strong Acid: $HCl(aq) \rightarrow H^+(aq) + Cl^-(aq)$ (100% ions)
Strong Base: $NaOH(aq) \rightarrow Na^+(aq) + OH^-(aq)$
notice the one way arrow

Weak Acid: $CH_3COOH(aq) \rightleftharpoons CH_3COO^-(aq) + H^+(aq)$ (~1% ions)
Weak Base: $NH_3(aq) + H_2O(l) \rightleftharpoons NH_4^+(aq) + Cl^-(aq)$
notice the equilibrium arrow!

Exam Hint

Only weak acids and bases have dissociation constants, (K_a or K_b), strong acids and bases do not have dissociation constants.

Strong and Weak are categories of acids and bases - you cannot "weaken" a substance by adding water - that's diluting it. Don't confuse concentration with strength.
Concentration is the solute / solvent ratio and can be changed by adding water (to dilute).
Strength is a category of electrolyte (acid or base), and cannot be changed. Acid and bases are either strong or weak.

Category	Concentrated	Dilute
Strong	12.0 M HCl(aq)	0.1 M HCl(aq)
Weak	16.0 M CH_3COOH(aq)	0.5 M CH_3COOH(aq)

Distinguishing between Strong and Weak.

In a strong acid the concentration of $H^+(aq)$ is the same as the stated concentration of the substance. However, due to only partial dissociation, a weak acid has much less $H^+(aq)$ than the amount stated.
For example, a 0.1 M CH_3COOH solution has an $H^+(aq)$ concentration of only 0.00134 M - almost 100 times less!

So in "equimolar" solutions, we have much lower $[H^+(aq)]$ in the weak acid compared to the strong acid.

We can do some quick chemical tests to tell the difference - based on the amount of $H^+(aq)$ present. - Remember that rate depends on concentration.

Test	Strong Acid	Weak Acid
add reactive metal eg Mg	**fast** H_2 production	**slow** H_2 production
add a carbonate, CO_3^{2-}	**fast** CO_2 production	**slow** CO_2 production
conductivity	high (many ions)	low (few ions)
pH of 0.1 M solution	=1	≈ 3 - 4

Table 8.2: Chemical tests for Strong and Weak Acids

pH Scale

pH is defined as $pH = -log[H^+(aq)]$

Definition

Every step in the pH scale represents a factor of ten change in the concentration of H^+ ions.

pH	$[H^+(aq)]$	pOH	$[OH^-(aq)]$	$[H^+(aq)] \times [OH^-(aq)]$	pOH + pH
1	1×10^{-1}	13	1×10^{-13}	1×10^{-14}	14
3	1×10^{-3}	11	1×10^{-11}	1×10^{-14}	14
5	1×10^{-5}	9	1×10^{-9}	1×10^{-14}	14
7	1×10^{-7}	7	1×10^{-7}	1×10^{-14}	14
9	1×10^{-9}	5	1×10^{-5}	1×10^{-14}	14
11	1×10^{-11}	3	1×10^{-3}	1×10^{-14}	14
13	1×10^{-13}	1	1×10^{-1}	1×10^{-14}	14

Table 8.3: Relationship between pH, pOH, $[H^+(aq)]$ and $[OH^-(aq)]$

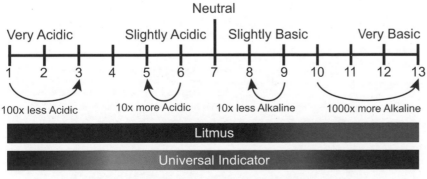

Figure 8.4: The pH Scale and Indicator colours

Summary Questions.

1. Write balanced equations for
   a) nitric acid and copper(II) oxide
   b) aluminium and hydrochloric acid
   c) iron(III) carbonate and sulphuric acid

2. Write the conjugate acid for the following bases

   a) SO_4^{2-} b) CO_3^{2-} c) $CH_3CO_2^-$

   d) NH_2^- e) NH_3 f) HPO_4^{2-}

3. Write the conjugate base for the following acids

   a) HI b) H_2 c) NH_4+

   d) HNO_2 e) $H_2PO_4^-$ f) H_3PO_4

4. Identify the conjugate pairs in the following equations
   a) $HSO_4^- + SO_3^{2-} \rightleftharpoons HSO_3^- + SO_4^{2-}$

   b) $S^{2-} + H_2O \rightleftharpoons HS^- + OH^-$

   c) $CN^- + H_3O^+ \rightleftharpoons HCN + H_2O$

   d) $H_2Se + H_2O \rightleftharpoons HSe^- + H_3O^+$

CHAPTER 9

OXIDATION & REDUCTION

Introduction

Oxidation & Reduction - "*Redox*" to chemists - reactions are those that involve a transfer of electrons.
Don't all reactions involve a transfer of electrons? – NO! Acid/Base reactions and precipitation reactions do not involve a transfer of electrons.

Definition

	Oxidation	Reduction
Oxygen	*Gain of oxygen*	*loss of oxygen*
Electrons	**Loss of electrons**	**Gain of electrons**
Hydrogen	*Loss of hydrogen*	*gain of hydrogen*
Electrode	**Anode**	**Cathode**
oxidation number	**increasing positive**	**decreasing postive**

In IB Chemistry, we are mostly concerned with the electronic definition of oxidation and reduction. The oxygen and hydrogen are included as additional information. - The hydrogen definition should be familiar to biologists.

Exam Hint

My favourite way to remember this is "**AN OIL RIG CAT**" - **AN**ode is the electrode where **O**xidation **I**s **L**oss of electrons occurs, and **R**eduction **I**s **G**ain of electrons at the **CAT**hode.

Oxidation numbers.

Oxidation numbers are chemists' way to keep an account of electrons.

Rules for Determining Oxidation Numbers

1. The oxidation number of any free element is zero, regardless of how complex its molecules might be.

2. The oxidation number of any simple, monatomic ion is equal to the charge on the ion.

3. The sum of all the oxidation numbers of the atoms in a molecule is equal to the charge on the particle (neutral for molecules, ionic charge for complex ions.)

4. In its compounds, group I and II metals have an oxidation number of +1 and +2 respectively.

5. In its compounds, fluorine has an oxidation number of –1.

6. In its compounds, hydrogen usually has an oxidation number of +1 (except $LiAlH_4$ H= –1)

7. In its compounds, oxygen has an oxidation number of –2. (Except the peroxide ion: O_2^{2-})

* When two rules conflict, take the rule with the lower number.

Students should be organized in their working for determining oxidation numbers.

Write the oxidation number for "each" atom on the top.

Write the total contribution for that element below.

each $_{+6}$ $_{-2}$
$$Cr_2O_7^{2-}$$
total $_{+12}$ $_{-14}$ = - 2

It's the bottom numbers that have to add to zero (or the

overall ionic charge).

Determine the oxidation number (state) of the element in **bold** type.

$+4$ $+3$ -6

MoS$_2$ **Ni**$_2$O$_3$ **P**$_4$O$_6$ **As**$_2$O$_3$

$+2$

Cr(NO$_3$)$_3$ **Cr**$_2$(SO$_4$)$_3$ **Cr**SO$_4$ **Cr**(SO$_4$)$_3$

ClO$^-$ **Cl**O$_2^-$ **Cl**O$_3^-$ **Cl**O$_4^-$

Redox Reactions

A redox reaction is one that has changes in oxidation number.

There are lots of reactions which are not redox reactions – precipitations, acid/base reactions etc.

Reactions that are always going to be redox reactions
- Combustion reactions – elemental oxygen becoming a compound
- Synthesis reactions – any element reacting with another to produce a compound
- Ions changing charge – Fe^{2+} becoming Fe^{3+}
- Ions of the oxy-acids changing the number of oxygen atoms – SO_3^{2-} becoming SO_4^{2-}

A fast way to pick off 99% of redox reactions is to look for an element (O_2, Cl_2, Fe, Na etc) as a reactant or product. This works because the oxidation state of any free element is zero, and in a compound, it is seldom zero.

Determine if the following reactions are oxidation-reduction reactions by determining any changes in oxidation number.

1. $H_2 + Cl_2 \rightarrow 2HCl$

2. $2KCl + MnO_2 + 2H_2SO_4 \rightarrow K_2SO_4 + MnSO_4 + Cl_2 + 2H_2O$

3. $CH_4(g) + 2O_2(g) \rightarrow CO_2(g) + 2H_2O(g)$

4. $Cr_2O_7^{2-}(aq) + 2OH^-(aq) \rightarrow 2CrO_4^{2-}(aq) + H_2O(aq)$

5. $Al(OH)_4^-(aq) \rightarrow AlO_2^-(aq) + 2H_2O(l)$

> *Oxidizing agent – a species that removes electrons from another.*
>
> *Reducing agent – a species that donates electrons to another.*

Common Oxidizing Agents	Common Reducing Agents
MnO_4^- (acidic, basic or neutral)	NaHSO$_3$
$Cr_2O_7^{2-}$ (acidified)	LiAlH$_4$
H_2O_2 (acidic, basic or neutral)	$S_2O_3^{2-}$

Table 9.1: Some common Oxidizing & Reducing Agents

Identify the oxidizing and reducing agents from the previous learning check.

Reactivity

Reactivity is always compares elements to each other, not their ions.

Reactivity of the Halogens - See Chapter 3 for more details.

Metals have an order of reactivity that you are not expected to memorise, but rather you may be asked to deduce an order of reactivity given some reactions.

Example

Determine the order of reactivity given the following reactions.

$$Mg(s) + Zn^{2+}(aq) \rightarrow Mg^{2+}(aq) + Zn(s)$$
$$Fe(s) + Cu^{2+}(aq) \rightarrow Cu(s) + Fe^{2+}(aq)$$
$$Zn(s) + Fe^{2+}(aq) \rightarrow Zn^{2+}(aq) + Fe(s)$$

Mg is more reactive than Zn.
Fe is more reactive than Cu.
Zn is more reactive than Fe.

Therefore the metals in order of their reactivity is Mg>Zn>Fe>Cu

Half Reactions

Because electrons are transferred, for any oxidation, something must be reduced, and vice versa.
We can write each of these processes separately, but including the electrons

reduction half reaction: $Cl_2 + 2e^- \rightarrow 2Cl^-$
oxidation half reaction: $Na \rightarrow Na^+ + e^-$

Just like in Hess' law, we need to add these two half reactions together to make a whole reaction. The trick is that the electrons must cancel out, so we need to double the sodium half reaction.

Reduction $Cl_2(g) + \cancel{2e^-} \rightarrow 2Cl^-$
Oxidation $\underline{2Na(g) \qquad \rightarrow 2Na^{\pm}(g) + \cancel{2e^-}}$
Net reaction $2Na(g) + Cl_2(g) \rightarrow 2NaCl(s)$

Voltaic Cells

A voltaic cell allows a chemical reaction to produce electricity based on difference in reactivity. The greater the difference in reactivity the greater the potential difference (voltage)

If one were to place a reactive metal into a solution of a less reactive metal, the electron transfer would occur at the interface of the two materials – i.e. If you dipped a zinc rod into a solution of copper(II) ions, the electrons in the zinc metal would transfer directly to the copper(II) ions and therefore cannot be harnessed to do any useful work.

In a Voltaic (also known as a Galvanic Cell), you must keep the two half reactions separate so that the electrons are forced to travel through an external circuit where they can do useful work.

The anode is defined as the electrode where oxidation occurs
The cathode is defined as the electrode where reduction occurs.

Definition

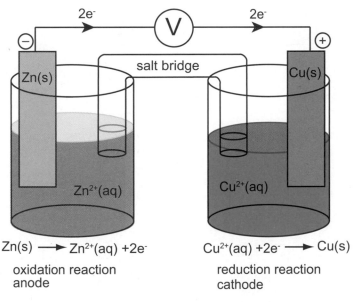

$Zn(s) \longrightarrow Zn^{2+}(aq) + 2e^-$

oxidation reaction
anode

$Cu^{2+}(aq) + 2e^- \longrightarrow Cu(s)$

reduction reaction
cathode

Cell Drawing Check List

- electrodes labelled with metal type
- electrodes immersed in solution of metal ions
- external circuit
- salt bridge (in solutions)
- half reactions
- anode / cathode labelled
- electrode polarity labelled
- electron flow in external circuit shown

no need to be in 3d though!

Figure 9.2: The Zinc/Copper Cell

Observations: The zinc electrode will gradually dissolve / lose mass as the solid is oxidized. The copper solution will lose it's blue colour (fades to colourless), and the copper electrode gains mass as copper ions are deposited.

Salt Bridge

You may explain the purpose of the salt bridge in any of the following ways…
- The salt bridge completes the circuit.
- The salt bridge allows for the conduction of **ions**.
- The salt bridge allows for the balancing of ionic charge.

Do not say that *electrons* flow through the salt bridge. – NO, NO, NO. ELECTRONS flow through the wire in the external circuit.

IONS flow through the salt bridge.

Common
Mistake:

Electrolysis of molten salts

An electrolytic cell uses a potential difference (electricity) to force (an otherwise non-spontaneous) reaction to occur. (cf Voltaic Cells)

When a molten (melted) salt is electrolysed, the positive ion (cation) migrates towards the negative electrode where it is discharged by reduction by gaining electrons from the electrode (cathode).

The negative ion (anion) migrates towards the positive electrode where it is discharged by oxidation by losing electrons to the electrode (anode)

Because there are no other elements around, and salts always have a metal and non-metal, it's easy to figure out the product.

Be Careful

Candidates often forget to write the correct formula of the elements - remember that halogens, hydrogen and oxygen are diatomic.

Wrong answer   Correct Answer
$NaCl(l) \rightarrow Na + Cl$ $2NaCl(l) \rightarrow 2Na(l) + Cl_2(g)$
                             Use state symbols too!

Summary questions

1. *Determine the oxidation numbers of the elements in bold type.*

   CO   **C**O_2 **Hg**$_2$**Cl**$_2$ **Hg**O

   K**Mn**O_4 Mg_2**P**$_2O_7$ **Xe**O**F**$_4$ **As**$_4$

   Na_2**C**$_2O_4$ Na_2**S**$_2O_3$ H**As**O_2 **S**$_8$

2. *Balance the following acidic oxidation – reduction reactions.*
   a) $H_2O_2 + Fe^{2+} \rightarrow Fe^{3+} + H_2O_2$
   b) $S_2O_3{}^{2-} + I_2 \rightarrow I^- + S_4O_6{}^{2-}$

3. *Determine whether the following reactions are spontaneous. If they are not, re-write the spontaneous equation – determine the cell potential for the spontaneous reaction.*
   a) $Cu^+(aq) + Fe^{3+}(aq) \rightarrow Cu^{2+}(aq) + Fe^{2+}(aq)$
   b) $2Br^-(aq) + Sn^{2+}(aq) \rightarrow Sn(s) + Br_2(aq)$
   c) $Ni^{2+}(aq) + Ag(s) \rightarrow Ni(s) + Ag^+(aq)$

CHAPTER 10

ORGANIC CHEMISTRY

Introduction

Organic chemistry is the study of carbon compounds. Carbon has the unique ability to form chains (concatenate). Because these chains can have branches and other atoms present, there are more organic chemicals than all other combined.

Carbon has a valence of four - that is, it always makes four bonds. Despite how simple this is, there are many students who make simple avoidable mistakes.

Hydrocarbons

Hydrocarbons are compounds that contain only carbon and hydrogen (not water - that's a carbohydrate!). If a hydrocarbon is bonded to the maximum number of hydrogens, then we say it is saturated. Saturated hydrocarbons have only single carbon-carbon bonds.

Hydrocarbon chains may be straight or branched, and may or may not contain double or triple bonds.

	Alkanes	Alkenes	Alkynes
General Formula	C_nH_{2n+2}	C_nH_{2n}	C_nH_{2n-2}
Bonding	single bonds	at least one double bond	at least one triple bond
Geometry*	tetrahedral	planar triangle	linear
C-4 example	butane C_4H_{10}	butene C_4H_8	butyne C_4H_6
Saturation	saturated	unsaturated	unsaturated
2 carbon Lewis structure	ethane	ethene	ethyne

Table 10.1: Hydrocarbon properties

*   The shape only applies to a specific carbon atom. In an pentene for instance, only the two carbons involved in the double bond are have planar triangular geometry, the others will have a tetrahedral geometry.

Homologous Series

*A homologous series is a group of compounds whose **successive** members differ by CH_2.*

(Note: <u>not</u> <u>all</u> members differ by CH_2, just the ones next to each other.)

n	Name	Molecular formula	Condensed structural formula
1	methane	CH_4	CH_4
2	ethane	C_2H_6	CH_3-CH_3
3	propane	C_3H_8	$CH_3-CH_2-CH_3$
4	butane	C_4H_{10}	$CH_3-CH_2-CH_2-CH_3$
5	pentane	C_5H_{12}	$CH_3-CH_2-CH_2-CH_2-CH_3$
6	hexane	C_6H_{14}	$CH_3-CH_2-CH_2-CH_2-CH_2-CH_3$

Table 10.2: Alkane homologous series

What's important to remember is that homologous series have similar chemical properties and display a gradual change in physical properties

Name	Formula	Boiling point (˚C)	Density (g/cm³)	ΔH_{vap} (kJ/mol)
methane	CH_4	-161.6	0.000717	8.16
ethane	C_2H_6	-88.6	0.001212	14.64
propane	C_3H_8	-42.1	0.00183	18.71
butane	C_4H_{10}	-0.5	0.00248	22.36
pentane	C_5H_{12}	36.1	0.626	25.70
hexane	C_6H_{14}	69.0	0.655	27.10

Table 10.3: Physical Property trends in Alkanes

Remember that physical properties are governed by the intermolecular forces (hydrogen bonding, dipole-dipole attraction, van der Waal's forces). As the hydrocarbon chain becomes longer, the van der Waal's forces increase. There still may be also hydrogen bonding (acids & alcohols) or dipole interactions (esters, ketones, aldehydes).

As the chain increases...

- melting point increases for all compounds - due to increased van der Waal's forces.
- solubility of in water decreases for alcohols and acids, because the proportion of hydrogen bonding in the molecule decreases.

Naming Hydrocarbons.

The names of hydrocarbons can be intimidating, but there is a very simple system.

> Pick the **longest continuous chain** of carbon atoms and obtain its root name. This is not necessarily horizontally or left to right!!!!
>
> Number the chain (either from left to right or vice-versa) in order to have the **lowest possible numbers** for the different attached hydrocarbon groups.
>
> Name the hydrocarbon groups attached to the longest chain by changing the suffix -ane of the root name to - yl and indicate the point of attachment by the number of the carbon atom to which the group is attached. Common group names are:
>
> Methyl ($-CH_3$); ethyl ($-CH_2CH_3$)

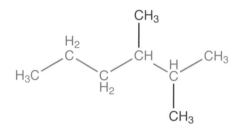

The molecule above is 2,3-dimethylhexane

There are many possible choices for branched groups - they could be alkyl chains (methyl, ethyl etc), or halogens (chloro, bromo, iodo)

> When two or more branches are present, you...
>
> Name them alphabetically
>
> Indicate the number of the same group by di, tri, etc, (not a factor in the alphabetical naming)
>
> Indicate the positions of the groups with numbers.
>
> Use comma's to separate numbers, and hyphens(-) to separate numbers and letters.

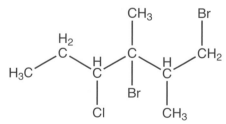

This is 1,3-dibromo-4-chloro-2,3-dimethylhexane

Select the longest carbon chain and rewrite so that the longest chain is horizontal. Write the name of the compound.

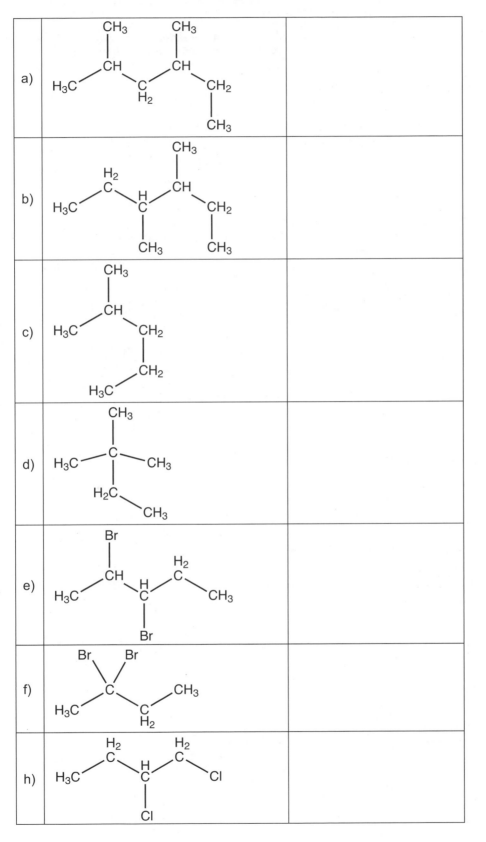

Isomers

Definition

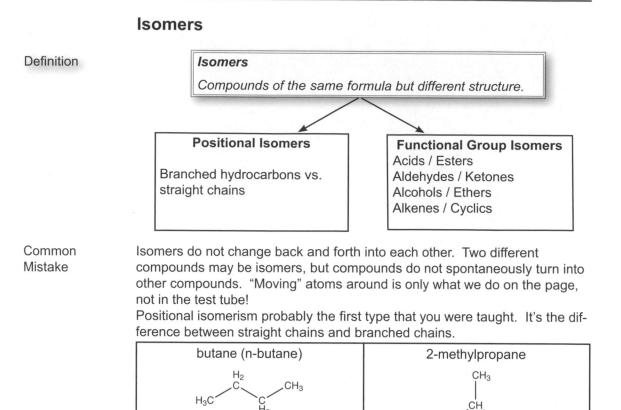

Isomers

Compounds of the same formula but different structure.

Positional Isomers	Functional Group Isomers
Branched hydrocarbons vs. straight chains	Acids / Esters Aldehydes / Ketones Alcohols / Ethers Alkenes / Cyclics

Common
Mistake

Isomers do not change back and forth into each other. Two different compounds may be isomers, but compounds do not spontaneously turn into other compounds. "Moving" atoms around is only what we do on the page, not in the test tube!

Positional isomerism probably the first type that you were taught. It's the difference between straight chains and branched chains.

butane (n-butane)	2-methylpropane

Table 10.4: The two isomers of C_4H_{10}

10.2 Learning
Check

Name and draw the 3 isomers of pentane, C_5H_{12}

Name and draw the 5 isomers of hexane, C_6H_{14}

You should be familiar with the four isomers of sbstituted butanes, as they represent structural isomers as well as the concept of positional isomers and compounds containing primary (1°), secondary (2°) and tertiary (3°) carbons.

The degree of substitution of a carbon indicates the number of branches that are attached to it. Primary carbons have only one branch - and are therefore at the end of a chain. Secondary carbons are in the middle of a chain. Tertiary carbons have three carbon chain branches. We usually identify the degree of a carbon bearing a halogen or an alcohol.

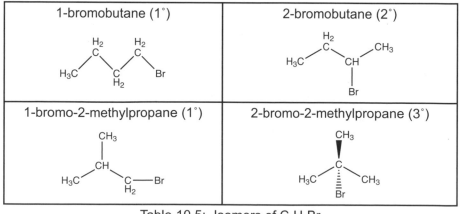

1-bromobutane (1°)	2-bromobutane (2°)
1-bromo-2-methylpropane (1°)	2-bromo-2-methylpropane (3°)

Table 10.5: Isomers of C_4H_9Br

Functional Group Isomerism

Isomerism can also give rise to different functional groups. It arises from the interchange of atoms that are specific to a functional group.
The following pairs are structural isomers - know them

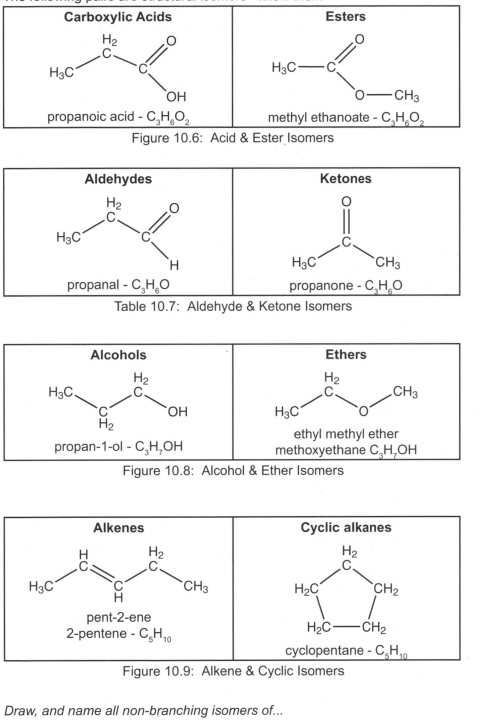

Carboxylic Acids	Esters
propanoic acid - $C_3H_6O_2$	methyl ethanoate - $C_3H_6O_2$

Figure 10.6: Acid & Ester Isomers

Aldehydes	Ketones
propanal - C_3H_6O	propanone - C_3H_6O

Table 10.7: Aldehyde & Ketone Isomers

Alcohols	Ethers
propan-1-ol - C_3H_7OH	ethyl methyl ether / methoxyethane C_3H_7OH

Figure 10.8: Alcohol & Ether Isomers

Alkenes	Cyclic alkanes
pent-2-ene / 2-pentene - C_5H_{10}	cyclopentane - C_5H_{10}

Figure 10.9: Alkene & Cyclic Isomers

Draw, and name all non-branching isomers of...

a) $C_4H_8O_2$

b) C_5H_8O

10.3 Learning
Check

Alkanes

Alkanes are the "backbone" of organic chemistry. They are generally unreactive. Their inert nature is due to the low electronegativity difference between carbon (2.4), and hydrogen (2.1). This makes the molecule non-polar. The carbon - hydrogen bond is also rather strong (412 kJ mol^{-1}). The strong bond is hard to break, so the chain often remains intact.
They provide a structure for chemists (and nature) to hang off more interesting reactive groups – functional groups.

There are however two types of reactions that alkanes undergo.

Combustion.

All alkanes completely combust when reacted with excess $O_2(g)$ to produce $CO_2(g)$ and $H_2O(g)$.
Incomplete combustion occurs when their isn't sufficient oxygen, and produces either carbon monoxide or carbon solid (soot)

complete: $\quad C_5H_{12} + 8O_2(g) \rightarrow 5CO_2(g) + 6H_2O(g)$
incomplete $\quad C_5H_{12} + {}^{11}/_2O_2(g) \rightarrow 5CO(g) + 6H_2O(g)$
incomplete $\quad C_5H_{12} + 3O_2(g) \rightarrow 5C(g) + 6H_2O(g)$

10.4 Learning Check *Write the balanced equations for the complete combustion of the first four alkanes.*

10.5 Learning Check *Write the balancee equations for the combustion of the first four alkanes producing carbon monoxide.*

Substitution

Alkanes can react with halogens in the presence of ultraviolet light to exchange a hydrogen for a halogen

$$CH_3CH_3(g) + Br_2(g) \xrightarrow{U.V.\ light} CH_3CH_2Br(g) + HBr$$

The ultraviolet light is required to break the Br–Br bond **homolytically**, producing two free radicals: Br•. As opposed to **heterolytically** which would produce Br$^+$ and Br$^-$.
The reactants are orange / brown due to the $Br_2(g)$ present, the products are colourless.

Br_2 + ultraviolet light $\rightarrow$ 2Br•   **production** of bromine radical
$CH_3CH_3 + Br• \rightarrow CH_3CH_2• + HBr$ **propagation** step
$CH_3CH_2• + Br_2 \rightarrow CH_3CH_2Br + Br•$ **propagation** step
$CH_3CH_2• + Br• \rightarrow CH_3CH_2Br$ **termination**: recombination of radicals

Substitution of more hydrogens can take place and eventually replace all H's with Br's.
This reaction needs the ultraviolet light (a test tube placed in sunlight is sufficient) in order to react.

This reaction needs the ultraviolet light (test tube placed in sunlight is sufficient) in order to react.

Organic Functional Groups

Functional Group	Type	Condensed Structural Formula	Structural Formula	4 carbon example
Hydrocarbons	Alkanes	R-CH_3	R—CH_3	Butane
	Alkenes	RCH=CH_2	R—CH=CH_2	2-Butene / But-2-ene
Alcohols	Primary (1°)	R-CH_2OH	R—CH_2—OH	1-Butanol / Butan-1-ol
	Secondary (2°)	R-$CH(OH)R'$	R—$CH(OH)$—R	2-Butanol / Butan-2-ol
Aldehydes	Aldehydes are always terminal	R-CHO	R—CHO	Butanal
Carboxylic Acids	Acids are always terminal	R-$COOH$	R—$COOH$	Butanoic Acid
Ketones	Ketones are always secondary	R-CO-R'	R—CO—R	Butanone

IB Chemistry is not generally concerned with multifunctional compounds with the exception of condensation polymerization monomers. Therefore, if asked to draw the possible structures for a given formula, ONLY USE THE ABOVE FUNCTIONAL GROUPS.

Students often draw "enols" as an isomer of $C_nH_{2n}O$. An enol contains a C=C and alcohol in the same molecule. DO NOT USE THESE. If you draw one, you will get yourself on a path where the rest of the question stops making sense. You should draw an aldehyde or a ketone.

Students often draw "enols" as an isomer of $C_nH_{2n}O$. An enol contains a C=C and alcohol in the same molecule. DO NOT USE THESE. If you draw one, you will get yourself on a path where the rest of the question stops making sense. You should draw an aldehyde or a ketone.

Alkenes — Addition Reactions

Alkenes are a basic starting point for organic chemistry as they have a region of accessible attractive electron density. The double bond in ethene has a big fat juicy area of electrons that can react with other compounds.

Figure 10.10: The reactive double bond in ethene

1. Hydrogenation (requires a catalyst of Ni, Pd, or Pt)

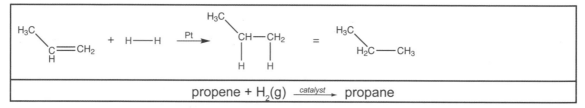

propene + H_2(g) $\xrightarrow{catalyst}$ propane

2. Halogenation

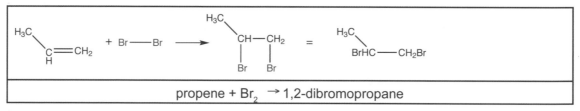

propene + Br_2 $\rightarrow$ 1,2-dibromopropane

3. Addition of HX

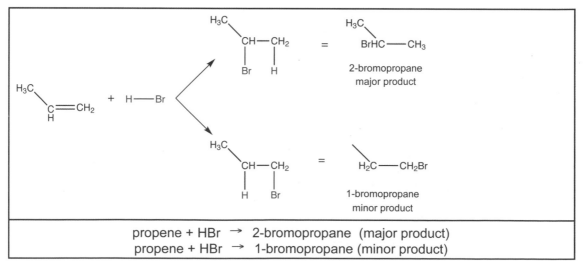

propene + HBr $\rightarrow$ 2-bromopropane (major product)
propene + HBr $\rightarrow$ 1-bromopropane (minor product)

4. Hydration - Addition of water.

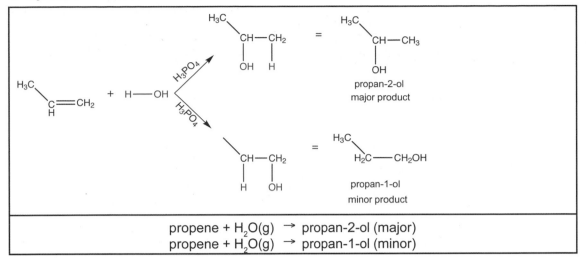

propene + H_2O(g) → propan-2-ol (major)
propene + H_2O(g) → propan-1-ol (minor)

5. Addition Polymerization

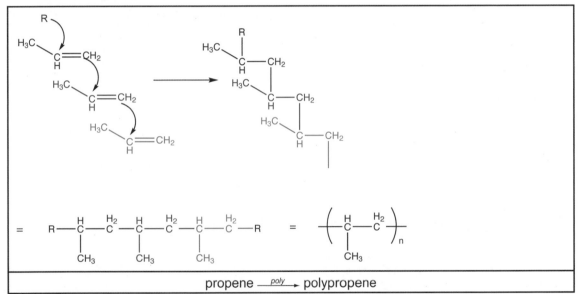

propene —*poly*→ polypropene

Be careful with the drawing of the polymer. **The polymer chain is built of only the two carbons involving the double bond.** All other parts of the molecule are branches off of the chain. In the example of polypropene, there is a methyl group branching off of the main polymer chain every two carbons.

Below are some examples of addition monomers and their corresponding polymers.

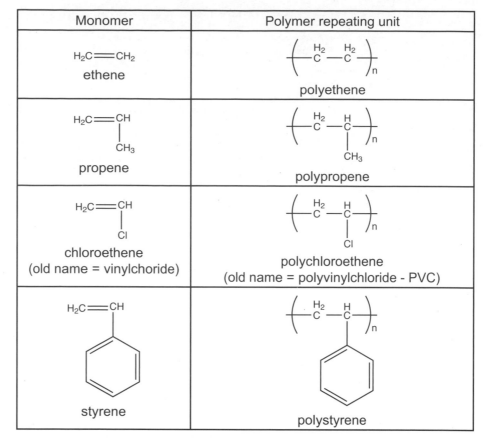

Monomer	Polymer repeating unit
H₂C=CH₂ ethene	polyethene
H₂C=CH with CH₃ propene	polypropene
H₂C=CH with Cl chloroethene (old name = vinylchloride)	polychloroethene (old name = polyvinylchloride - PVC)
H₂C=CH with benzene ring styrene	polystyrene

Table 10.11: Examples of monomers and polymers

10.6 Learning Check

Draw the polymer repeating unit for the following monomers.

a) *but-2-ene*
b) *but-1-ene*

Alcohols

Alcohols are the homologous series that contain an OH group.
The difference between NaOH and alcohols is that NaOH is ionic and dissociates into $Na^+(aq)$ and OH^- (aq) ions, whereas C–OH is covalent and does not dissociate – It's a molecule.
Short chain alcohols are soluble in water due to the hydrogen bonding of the OH group. As the chain lengthens, the solubility decreases because the proportion of hydrogen bonding in the molecule is overwhelmed by the van der Waal's forces.

n	name	molecular formula	condensed structural formula	b.p	Solubility
1	methanol	CH_3OH	CH_3OH	65°C	miscible
2	ethanol	C_2H_5OH	CH_3-CH_2-OH	78°C	miscible
3	propan-1-ol	C_3H_7OH	CH_3-CH_2-CH_2-OH	97°C	miscible
4	butan-1-ol	C_4H_9OH	CH_3-CH_2-CH_2-CH_2-OH	118°C	9.1 g /100 g H_2O
5	pentan-1-ol	$C_5H_{11}OH$	CH_3-CH_2-CH_2-CH_2-CH_2-OH	138°C	2.7 g /100 g H_2O
6	hexan-1-ol	$C_6H_{13}OH$	CH_3-CH_2-CH_2-CH_2-CH_2-CH_2-OH	151°C	slightly soluble

Table 10.12: Homologous Series of Alcohols

Combustion of alcohols

Alcohols can be combusted - usually completely.
When balancing, don't forget about the oxygen in the alcohol.

Write balanced equations for the complete combustion of the first four alcohols.

10.7 Learning
Check

Oxidation of alcohols

Alcohols may be oxidized by a variety of agents. The common one in IB Chemistry is "acidified potassium dichromate" or if you prefer $H^+/K_2Cr_2O_7$. (It needs to be acidic for it to work!)
Depending on the structure of your alcohol, you get different products, or none at all.
Primary alcohols can be oxidized to aldehydes, which can then be further oxidized to carboxylic acids. In all cases, the functional groups are terminal (at the end of the chain)
Secondary alcohols have an alcohol group in the middle of the chain, and can be oxidized to form ketones, which cannot be further oxidized.
Tertiary alcohols cannot be oxidized.

	Ox. agent	1st Product	Ox agent	2nd Product
1°	$H^+(aq)/Cr_2O_7^{2-}$ (aq)	aldehyde	$H^+(aq)/Cr_2O_7^{2-}$ (aq)	carboxylic acid
2°	$H^+(aq)/Cr_2O_7^{2-}$ (aq)	ketone	$H^+(aq)/Cr_2O_7^{2-}$ (aq)	none
3°	$H^+(aq)/Cr_2O_7^{2-}$ (aq)	none		

What you see during the oxidation is the oxidizing agent – the orange $Cr_2O_7^{2-}$ ion changing to the green Cr^{3+} ion (as the dichromate ion is reduced)
Remember to state the <u>change of colour</u> – *"orange to green"*. This is also a way to chemically distinguish tertiary alcohols from primary or secondary.

Alcohol Oxidation Products

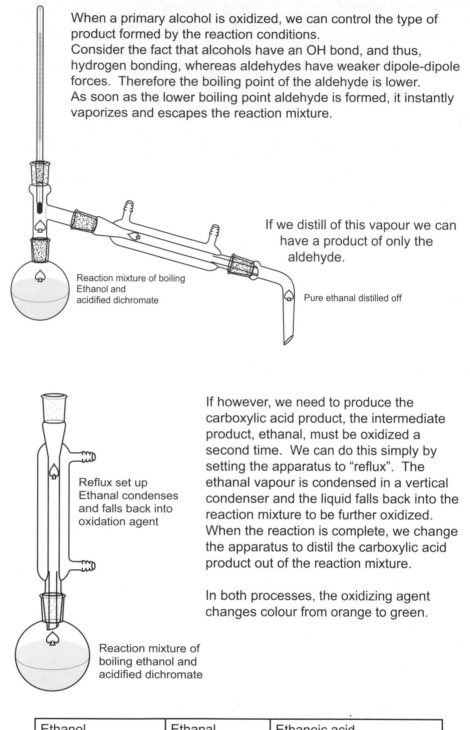

When a primary alcohol is oxidized, we can control the type of product formed by the reaction conditions.
Consider the fact that alcohols have an OH bond, and thus, hydrogen bonding, whereas aldehydes have weaker dipole-dipole forces. Therefore the boiling point of the aldehyde is lower.
As soon as the lower boiling point aldehyde is formed, it instantly vaporizes and escapes the reaction mixture.

If we distill of this vapour we can have a product of only the aldehyde.

Reaction mixture of boiling Ethanol and acidified dichromate

Pure ethanal distilled off

If however, we need to produce the carboxylic acid product, the intermediate product, ethanal, must be oxidized a second time. We can do this simply by setting the apparatus to "reflux". The ethanal vapour is condensed in a vertical condenser and the liquid falls back into the reaction mixture to be further oxidized. When the reaction is complete, we change the apparatus to distil the carboxylic acid product out of the reaction mixture.

In both processes, the oxidizing agent changes colour from orange to green.

Reflux set up
Ethanal condenses and falls back into oxidation agent

Reaction mixture of boiling ethanol and acidified dichromate

Ethanol	Ethanal	Ethanoic acid
hydrogen bonding	dipole forces	strong hydrogen bonding
b.p. = 78°C	b.p. = 20°C	b.p. = 118°C

Halogenoalkanes

Some of the halogenoalkanes are generally not very reactive. They get used as a variety of solvents which can end up in the upper atmosphere and cause ozone damage – but that's an Option topic.

The reactivity of those that do react is caused by the polarity of the carbon - halogen bond due to the high electronegativity of the halogen. This polarity allows the carbon atom to be partially positive (∂+) and therefore be susceptible to attack by something that is attracted to a partially positive charge – a nucleophile.

Draw and name all 16 isomers of chlorohexane, $C_6H_{13}Cl$. Identify each as primary, secondary or tertiary with regards to the halogen bearing carbon.

10.8 Learning Check

Nucleophilic Substitution reactions

In a nucleophilic substitution reaction, a "nucleophile" replaces a "leaving group".

Nucleophile: an ion or molecule with at least one lone pair of electrons which, is attracted to a partial positive charge centre.
(NOTE: not attracted to "a nucleus")

Definition

In general a hydroxide ion displaces a halogen from a molecule.

$$OH^- + R—X \rightarrow R—OH + X^-$$

There are two different mechanisms through which this substitution can occur. One uses first order kinetics, and is termed S_N1, the other uses second order kinetics and is termed S_N2.

S$_N$1 – Substitution- nucleophilic – First order kinetics

The steps in the mechanism are as follows...
1. Dissociation of the leaving group (the halogen) to leave an ionic intermediate. This is the slow step. Rate = k[CR$_3$X]
2. Attack by a nucleophile eg. :OH⁻.

Exam Hint
Be able to draw the entire
mechanism shown here

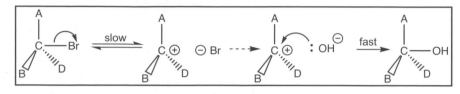

Figure 10.13: S$_N$1 reaction mechanism

Important details
1. The rate of reaction depends only upon the dissociation of the leaving group - this is the slow step.
2. The intermediate is ionic – it is stabilized by protic solvents (like water).
3. The intermediate is a carbocation (positive charge)

S$_N$2 – Substitution – nucleophilic – Second order kinetics

The steps in the mechanism are as follows...
1. Attack by the nucleophile on the substrate
2. Dissociation of the leaving group.

Exam Hint
Be able to draw the entire
mechanism shown here

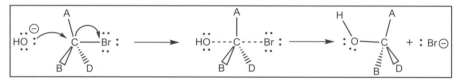

Figure 10.14: S$_N$2 Reaction Mechanism

Important details
1. The rate of reaction depends on the concentration of both the nucleophile and the halogenoalkane. Rate=k[CR$_3$X][Nu]
2. The intermediate is non-ionic, and is stabilized by aprotic solvents, like propanone.
3. The intermediate has three full strength bonds, and two partial bonds.
4. As the charge density (bond) between the nucleophile and the substrate increases, the charge density between the substrate and the leaving group decreases. – one fades in the other fades out.
5. The nucleophile must attack from the side opposite the leaving group.

Which Mechanism? S$_N$1 or S$_N$2 – the factors affecting the dominant mechanism.

Factor	S$_N$1	S$_N$2
Solvent	protic - water	aprotic – like propanone
Structure	3°/ Tertiary carbons	1°/ Primary carbons
Branching	Bulky / branched chains prevent backside attack. This is called "stearic hindrance".	Linear side chains or hydrogen allow space for nucleophile to attack first.

Reaction Pathways

Reaction pathways refer to the combination of two reactions that lead to a desired product from a specific starting material.

The key is that you need to know all the products and reactants so that you can determine a reasonable intermediate product.

You may be required to state...

- the conditions for the first reaction
- the isolation / collection of the intermediate product
- the name and structure of the intermediate product
- the type of intermolecular forces for the intermediate product
- the conditions for the second reaction
- the isolation / collection of the final product
- the type of intermolecular forces for the final product
- the relative boiling points of each of the three species

Here are six possibilities - refer to your syllabus, pg 67 to see if there are any others.

1. alkene $\rightarrow$ alcohol $\rightarrow$ aldehyde
2. alkene $\rightarrow$ alcohol $\rightarrow$ ketone
3. alkene $\rightarrow$ alcohol $\rightarrow$ carboxylic acid
4. alkene $\rightarrow$ halogenoalkane $\rightarrow$ alcohol
5. alkane $\rightarrow$ halogenoalkane $\rightarrow$ dihalogenoalkane
6. halogenoalkane $\rightarrow$ alcohol $\rightarrow$ aldehyde

The general reactions are...

	Reactant	Reaction	intermediate	reaction	product
1.	alkene	hydration	1° alcohol	oxidation & distillation	aldehyde
2.	alkene	hydration	2° alcohol	oxidation	ketone
3.	alkene	hydration	1° alcohol	oxidation & reflux	carboxylic acid
4.	alkene	addition of HBr	bromoalkane	S_N1/S_N2 with OH^-	alcohol
5.	alkane	substitution Br_2 and UV	bromoalkane	substitution Br_2 and UV	dibromoalkane
6.	bromo-alkane	S_N1	1° alcohol	oxidation & distillation	aldehyde

Make sure that you know the conditions required for each of the reactions above.

State the reactions and conditions needed to produce butan-2-one from but-2-ene.

10.9 Learning Check

State the reactions and conditions needed to produce propanal from 1-bromopropane.

Summary Questions

1. The following names are incorrect. Draw the structure and correctly name it.
   a) 2-ethylpropane
   b) 1-methylbutane
   c) 3-methylbutane
   d) 2,3-diethylbutane

2. Compound P has the formula $C_4H_{10}O$ and could exist as 4 different isomers.

   a) Name and draw all four isomers of P.

   b) i) One of the isomers of P may be oxidized to produce a non-acidic compound. Draw   the molecule and name it.
      ii) State the conditions for this reaction.

   c) Another isomer of P cannot be oxidized. Name this isomer.

   d) Two of the isomers of P may be oxidized to produce carboxylic acids.
      i) What conditions are used to produce the acids?
      ii) Name and draw the two acid isomers.

   e) Compound P can be formed by two different types of nucleophilic substitution   mechanisms.
      i) What is meant by the term "nucleophilic substitution"
      ii) Write a chemical equation for this reaction.
      iii) Determine the isomer that was formed by an Sn1 reaction. Choose an appropriate   starting material (Q) and draw the mechanism.
      iv) Identify the isomers of P that were formed by an Sn2 reaction. Draw and name the   starting materials.

CHAPTER 11

MEASUREMENT & DATA PROCESSING

Uncertainty in Measurements

Unlike in Mathematics, numbers in Science are measurements. They result from the comparison of the magnitude of some quality against a standard. The quality of the measuring device tells us how precise our measurement can be and what the uncertainty is.

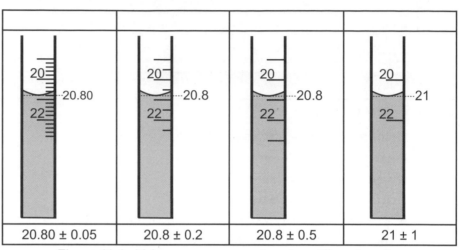

| 20.80 ± 0.05 | 20.8 ± 0.2 | 20.8 ± 0.5 | 21 ± 1 |

Figure 11.1: Volume measurements using different scales

Precision & Accuracy

Accuracy is the degree of exactness that the measurement has to the "true" value.

Precision refers to the degree of exactness which a measuring instrument can determine accuracy.

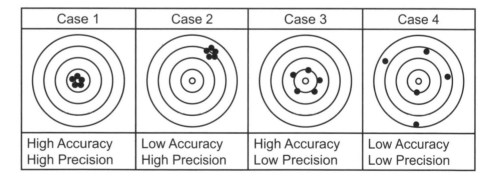

Case 1	Case 2	Case 3	Case 4
High Accuracy High Precision	Low Accuracy High Precision	High Accuracy Low Precision	Low Accuracy Low Precision

In case 1 - all shots hit very close to the center; all measurements are close to the true value, and each other.

In case 2 - all shots hit close to each other, but for some reason there is a systematic (consistent) error causing the shots to miss the centre; all measurements agree with each other, but they don't agree with the "true" value.

In case 3, it appears that our "average" shot has hit the bullseye, but no individual shot hits the bullseye. Repeated measurements may be of help to zero in on the "true" value.

In case 4, a larger lack of precision has prevented even our "average" from being useful.

Significant Digits

Rules

All non-zero digits are significant.

"Captive" zeros (zeros between non-zero digits) are significant.

Leading zeros are never significant.

Trailing zeros...

      a) are not significant if they are place holders (left of a decimal).

      b) are significant if they indicate a measurement (right of a decimal).

Exact numbers (counting numbers) have unlimited significant digits.

Examples

a)	200	one s.f.	=2	$\times 10^2$
b)	202	three s.f.	=2.02	$\times 10^2$
c)	200.0	four s.f.	=2.000	$\times 10^2$
d)	0.02	one s.f	=2	$\times 10^{-2}$
e)	0.0202	three s.f.	=2.02	$\times 10^{-2}$
f)	0.0200	three s.f.	=2.00	$\times 10^{-2}$

Determine the number of significant figures in the following measurements...   11.1 Learning
Check

   a) 4010   *b) 3.520*
   c) 0.00214   *d) 0.01010*
   e) 10.02   *f) 2.50 x 10³* (2.50×10^3)

Rounding off Numbers

Rules for Rounding Off

If the digit to be removed

a)   is less than 5 the preceding digit stays the same

b)   is 5 or greater, the preceding number is increased by 1.

DO NOT ROUND OFF RAW DATA; ONLY ROUND THE FINAL ANSWER.   Be
Careful

Round the following to the indicated number of significant digits.   11.2 Learning
Check
   a) 2150 (2 s.d.)   *b) 0.0346 (2 s.d.)*
   c) 1.994 (3 s.d.)   *d) 0.0256 (2 s.d.)*
   e) 0.0050129 (3 s.d.)   *f) 2149.99 (3 s.d.)*

Adding and Subtracting Significant Digits

Rules

Add up the digits by columns.

Round off the final answer to the same number of **decimal places** as the least precise number.

Examples

Example 1	Example 2	Example 3	Example 4
41.11	0.2129	101.4	1.0
20.5	0.002	25	2.04
+18.333	+0.03	+201	+5.03
79.943	=0.2449	327.4	=8.07
=79.9	=0.24	=327	=8.1

Multiplying and Dividing Significant Digits

Rules

Multiply the values as normal.

Round off the final answer to the same number of **significant digits** as the least precise number.

Examples

Example 1	Example 2	Example 3
2.5 (2 sd)	8.314 (4 sd)	35.45 (4 sd)
x 1.1111 (5 sd)	x 2.5x10^{-2} (2sd)	x2.25 (3 sd)
=2.77775	=0.20785	=79.7625
=2.8 (2 sd)	= 0.21 (2sd)	=79.8 (3 sd)

Exam Hint

The easiest way not lose points on the exam is to write the answer with the same number of significant digits as the information in the question.

11.3 Learning Check

Carry out the following calculations and express your answer with the appropriate number of significant figures.

a) 2.50 + 3.369   *b) 23.29 - 8.314*
c) 0.0250 + 2.5x10-3   *d) 0.10 - 0.061*
e) 8.314 x 101.325   *f) 35.45 x 0.075*
g) 2.50 ÷ 0.92   *h) 101000 ÷ 8.3*

Absolute & Relative Uncertainty

An uncertainty exists with every measurement.
The absolute uncertainty for any measuring device is the same for each
measurement. This is why you can state it in the heading of a data table.
On analogue devices (thermometers, glassware etc) it is commonly taken as
half of the smallest division.

Relative uncertainty is a measure of the uncertainty with respect to the
magnitude of the measurement. It is usually expressed as a percentage with
only one significant digit.
Calculate the relative uncertainty by dividing the absolute uncertainty by the
measurement and multiply by 100%. (You have to do it for each measurement; it's best to use a spreadsheet program)
Ideally we would like very low relative uncertainty. Then any uncertainty is
insignificant.

Propagating Uncertainty

The uncertainty of a calculation is always greater than the individual
uncertainties.

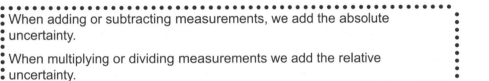

When adding or subtracting measurements, we add the absolute
uncertainty.

When multiplying or dividing measurements we add the relative
uncertainty.

Rules

Let's take a practical example.   Example

> *Determine the amount of heat required to raise the temperature of
> 75.00 g of water from 25.0°C to 85.5°C. The specific heat capacity of
> water is 4.18 J g^{-1}°C^{-1}. The uncertainties are ±0.005 g and ±0.5 °C.*

Solution
mass = 75.00 g ± 0.005 g
T_1 = 25.1°C ±0.5°C T_2 = 85.5°C ± 0.5°C

First of all we calculate ΔT = 60.4°C ± 1.0°C (add the abs. uncert.)

The next step requires us to use relative uncertainties. We convert
the absoute uncertainties into relative percent uncertainty.

mass: 0.005÷ 75.00x100% = 0.007% : 75.00 ± 0.007%
ΔT: 0.4 ÷ 60.4 x100% = 1.65% =2%: 60.4°C ± 2%

$Q = mc\Delta T$
Q = 75.00g ± 0.007% × 4.18 J g^{-1}°C^{-1} × 60.4°C ± 2%
Q = 18935.4 J ± 2.007%
Q = 18900 J ± 2%   We only report 1 sd in the uncertainty.
Q = 18900 J ± 400 J   We may want to convert back to absolute
Q = 18.9 kJ ± 0.4 kJ

In this example the uncertainty of ±0.5°C on the thermometer is much
greater than the uncertainty on the balance. You can ignore the uncertainty
of the balance.

Types of Relationships

Graphs tend to be linear or adjusted through mathmatical manipulations so that they are in the form of a straight line. This allows us to determine the intercepts and the slope which may have a signifcance.

Examples
- The "Charles' Law" graph uses the x-intercept to find absolute zero.
- The Arrhenius plot manipulates the equation so that we can use the slope of the line to determine the activation energy of a reaction.
- The Rate of reaction graphs can be used to calculate the rate at an instant by finding the slope of the tangent of the curve at an instant.

Another way to determine the validity of results is through correlation. Correlation is how close each point follows a trend line, and is a measure of the accuracy and precision of your data.

Case 1	Case 2	Case 3	Case 4
High Correlation Positive slope	High Correlation Negative slope	Low Correlation	No Correlation

In cases 1 & 2, the points all fall on the line, correlation is high.
In case 3, the points fall near the line, but not on it - correlation is low, but it does exist.
In case 4, which line is correct? - There is no clear trend. There is no correlation.

Learning Check 1.1

a) 1.2×10^{24} b) 7.53×10^{22}

c) 9.03×10^{23} d) 7.53×10^{20}

e) 7.53×10^{18} f) 2.74×10^{15}

g) 3.2×10^{24} h) 1.11×10^{22}

Learning Check 1.2

a) 100 mol b) 0.375 mol

c) 5.00 mol d) 1.25×10^{-3} mol

e) 5.75×10^{-6} mol f) 8.75×10^{-5} mol

g) 4.25×10^{-4} mol h) 1.74 mol

Learning Check 1.3

a) 58.44 g mol^{-1} b) 155.99 g mol^{-1}

c) 80.06 g mol^{-1} d) 110.98 g mol^{-1}

e) 310.98 g mol^{-1} f) 246.51 g mol^{-1}

g) 159.70 g mol^{-1} h) 149.12 g mol^{-1}

i) 60.06 g mol^{-1}

Learning Check 1.4

a) 63.6 g b) 167 g

c) 22.2 g d) 7.65×10^{-4} g

e) 0.415 g f) 4.03×10^{-6} g

g) 90.3 g h) 6.37×10^{-4} g

i) 245.2 g

Learning Check 1.5

a) 6.27×10^{-2} mol b) 8.31×10^{-2} mol

c) 7.04×10^{-2} mol d) 1.38×10^{-2} mol

e) 3.00×10^{-2} mol f) 6.86×10^{-1} mol

g) 9.885×10^{-2} mol h) 1.86×10^{-2} mol

i) 4.97×10^{-3} mol

Learning Check 1.6

a) $2K + 2H_2O \rightarrow H_2 + 2KOH$

b) $3CuO + 2NH_3 \rightarrow 3H_2O + N_2 + 3Cu$

c) $2Al + 6HCl \rightarrow 2AlCl_3 + 3H_2$

d) $2ZnS + 3O_2 \rightarrow 2ZnO + 2SO_2$

e) $2NH_4Cl + Ca(OH)_2 \rightarrow CaCl_2 + 2NH_3 + 2H_2O$

f) $2C_4H_{10} + 13O_2 \rightarrow 8CO_2 + 10H_2O$

g) $H_3PO_4 + 3NaOH \rightarrow Na_3PO_4 + 3H_2O$

h) $2C_2H_2 + 5O_2 \rightarrow 4CO_2 + 2H_2O$

i) $2KClO_3 \rightarrow 2KCl + 3O_2$

j) $2C_2H_6 + 7O_2 \rightarrow 4CO_2 + 6H_2O$

k) $N_2 + 3H_2 \rightarrow 2NH_3$

l) $N_2H_4 + O_2 \rightarrow N_2 + 2H_2O$

m) $2Na + Cl_2 \rightarrow 2NaCl$

n) $4Fe + 3O_2 \rightarrow 2Fe_2O_3$

o) $2SO_2 + O_2 \rightarrow 2SO_3$

Learning Check 1.7

1. a) 2.5 mol b) 15 mol

2. a) i) 15 mol ii) 100 mol

   iii) 2.5 mol

  b) 10.0 mol

  c) i) 12 mol ii) 80 mol

   iii) 2.0 mol

3. a) 62.5 mol

  b) 0.80 mol

  c) i) 2.48 mol ii) 0.275 mol

Learning Check 1.8

1. a) 2500 g of oxygen

  b) 558 g of ethanol

2. 703 g of iron(III) oxide

3. 1.72×10^{-2} g of silver sulphide

4. a) 2.86 kg of oxygen

  b) 3.29 kg of NO_2

5. a) 198 g of tungsten

  b) 6.53 g of hydrogen required.

Learning Check 1.9

1. a) n = 0.339 mol of ethane

   n = 1.39 mol of oxygen

  b) C_2H_6 is the limiting reactant

  c) 29.8 g of CO_2 produced

2. n=0.9 mol of NaOH

   n=0.122 mol of H_3PO_4

   a) H_3PO_4 is the limiting reactant

   b) 20.1 g of Na_3PO_4 are produced

3. a) $2C_4H_{10} + 13O_2 \rightarrow 8CO_2 + 10H_2O$

   b) n=3.125 mol of O_2

      n=1.72 mol of C_4H_{10}

   c) O_2 is the limiting reactant

   d) 84.63 g of CO_2 formed

      43.32 g of H_2O formed

Learning Check 1.10

a) 1.50 M b)   1.71 M

c) 0.0200 Md)   0.100 M

e) 41.5 g   f)   4.25 g

g) 1.00 g   h)   29.7 g

Learning Check 1.11

1. 88%

2. 81.77%

Learning Check 1.12

1. C_2H_5

2) C_3H_4

3. CH

Learning Check 1.13

1. CH_3

2. CH_2

3. C_3H_8

Learning Check 1.14

1. CH_2O

2. C_3H_8O

3. C_2H_4O

Summary Questions - Chapter 1

1. a) $AgNO_3(aq) + NaCl(aq) \rightarrow$

         $AgCl(s) + NaNO_3(aq)$

b) 3.00×10^{-3} mol AgCl(s)

c) 0.15 mol dm^{-3}

d) 35.1 g

2. a) CH

   b) 1.544×10^{-3} mol

      26.22 g mol^{-1}

   c) C_2H_2

   d) $CaC_2(s) + H_2O(l) \rightarrow$

         $Ca(OH)_2(aq) + C_2H_2(g)$

3. a) $n(C_7H_6O_3) = 4.34 \times 10^{-2}$ mol

      $n(C_4H_6O_3) = 4.90 \times 10^{-2}$ mol

   b) $C_7H_6O_3$ is the limiting reactant.

   c) 7.83 g of aspirin

   d) 83.5%

4. a) $2C_6H_{14} + 19O_2 \rightarrow 12CO_2 + 14H_2O$

   b) 5.22×10^{-2} mol hexane

      3.516×10^{-1} mol oxygen

   c) O_2 is the limiting reactant

   d) 9.77 g of CO_2 produced

      4.67 g of H_2O produced

   e) 1.41 g of unreacted C_6H_{14}

5. a) 5.000 mol of $BaSO_4(s)$

   b) 0.2000 mol dm^{-3}

   c) 0.1000 mol in 0.500 dm^3

   d) 109.9 g mol^{-1}

   e) Li

Learning Check 2.1

	A	Z	p	n	e
$_1^1H$	1	1	1	0	1
$_1^2H$	2	1	1	1	1
$_1^3H$	3	1	1	2	2
$_5^{10}B$	10	5	5	5	5
$_5^{11}B$	11	5	5	6	5
$_{17}^{35}Cl$	35	17	17	18	17
$_{17}^{37}Cl$	37	17	17	20	17

Learning Check 2.2

1. $107.96 = 108.0$

2. 24.3

3. 10.80

Learning Check 2.3

1. 31.5% ^{203}Tl; 68.5% ^{205}Tl

2. 6.00% ^6Li and 94.0% ^7Li

3. 64% ^{69}Ga; 36% ^{71}Ga

Chapter 2 Summary Questions

1. 109.5

2. 35% ^{89}Lm, 65% ^{90}Lm

3. a) 2,8,3

Learning Check 3.1

Larger	Explanation
O^{2-}	Increased e^-/ e^- repulsion or lower net attractive forces for same # of electrons
Mg	3 shells of electrons vs. 2 shells of electrons
F^-	Increased e^-/ e^- repulsion or lower net attractive forces for same # of electrons
K	4 shells of electrons vs. 3 shells of electrons
Ar	Lower nuclear charge on Ar, for same # of electrons
Na	3 shells in Na vs. 2 shells in Li
N	N has lower nuclear charge, therefore lower attraction between nucleus & e^-

Learning Check 3.2

a) Be, Mg, Ca   b) Xe, I, Te

c) Ge, Ga, In   d) F, N, As

e) F, Cl, S   f) Li, K, Cs

Learning Check 3.3

a) Li – fewest shells

b) P – fewer shells

c) O^+ - least e-/e- repulsion

d) Cl – greatest #protons for fewest shells

e) Ni – fewest shells

f) Ar – all have same # electrons, Ar has most protons

Learning Check 3.4

a) Mg^+ - still has 3 shells

b) O^- - more e-/e- repulsion

c) Ar, more e-/e- repulsion

d) Mg^+ - still has 3 shells

e) Al^{2+} - still has 3 shells

Learning Check 3.5

a) Ca, Mg, Be   b) Te, I, Xe

c) In, Ga, Ge   d) As, N, F

e) S, Cl, F   f) Cs K, Li

Chapter 3 Summary Questions

1 a2.   a) The I.E. decreases down the group. The greater number of shells means that the attractive force between the nucleus and the valence electron is less, so less energy is required to remove it

b) The I.E. increases across a period due to an increasing nuclear charge, and decreasing atomic radius

4. a) $2Li + I_2 \rightarrow 2LiI$

b) $2K + H_2O \rightarrow 2KOH + H_2$

c) $Br_2 + 2I^- \rightarrow 2Br^- + I_2$

Learning Check 4.1

a) Na_2S b) BeF_2

c) GaI_3 d) K_3N

e) AlP f) Mg_3N_2

Learning Check 4.2

a) copper(I) chloride

b) cobalt(II) iodide

c) chromium(III) oxide

d) nickel(III) bromide

e) manganese(IV) oxide

f) copper(1) sulphide

Learning Check 4.3

a) FeO

b) $HgCl_2$

c) Cu_2O

d) Ni_2O_3

e) $CoCl_2$

f) Fe_2S_3

Learning Check 4.4

a) NH_4Cl

b) $NaNO_3$

c) K_2CO_3

d) $CaSO_4$

e) $Mg_3(PO_4)_2$

f) $(NH_4)_2CO_3$

Learning Check 4.5

a) sodium hydrogen carbonate

b) sodium nitrite

c) ammonium nitrate

d) lithium phosphate

e) barium sulphate

f) ammonium sulphate

Learning Check 4.6

a) $FeSO_4$

b) $Ni(NO_3)_3$

c) $Cr(NO_3)_6$

d) Cu_2CO_3

e) $Hg(NO_3)_2$

f) $MnSO_4$

Learning Check 4.7

a) nickel(II) carbonate

b) copper(II) sulphate

c) iron(III) sulphate

d) cobalt(II) nitrate

e) nickel(III) nitrate

f) mercury(I) carbonat

Learning Check 4.8 & 4.9

a) trigonal pyramid

b) tetrahedral

c) tetrahedral

d) trigonal planar

e) bent / V-Shape

f) tetrahedral

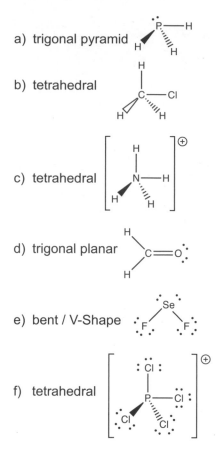

Chapter 4 Summary

1. a) calcium nitrate

   b) copper(II) nitrate

   b) aluminium sulphate

   d) iron(II) phosphate

   e) ammonium chloride

   f) sodium hydrogen carbonate

2. a) K_2O

   b) NH_4NO_3

   c) $MgCO_3$

   d) Ni_2O_3

   e) PbO_2

   f) $AlPO_4$

3. a)

   b)

   c)

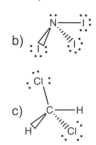

d)

e)

4. a) Hydrogen bonding

   b) Dipole forces

   c) Dipole forces

   d) Dipole forces

   e) Hydrogen bonging

   f) Dipole forces

5. NCl_3 has the higher melting point because of the dipole forces resulting from the asymmetry in the trigonal pyramidal geometry, due to its lone pair. BCl_3 is a planar triangle nonpolar molecule and therefore has a lower boiling point due to its Van der Waal's forces.

Learning Check 5.1

1. -134.8 kJ

2. -171.07 kJ

3. -98 kJ

4. -296.1 kJ

5. 226 kJ

Learning Check 5.2

1. -698 kJ mol⁻¹

2. -95 kJ mol⁻¹

3. -585 kJ mol⁻¹

4. -184 kJ mol⁻¹

5. -1774 kJ mol⁻¹

Chapter 5 Summary Questions

1. +322.2 kJ

2. -14.2 kJmol⁻¹

3. a) no change

   b) double ($\Delta T = 6.8°C$)

   c) no change

   d) less ($\Delta T = 2.27°C$)

Learning Check 7.1

1. $K_c = \dfrac{[H_2O]^2[SO_2]^2}{[H_2S]^2[O_2]^3}$

2. $K_c = \dfrac{[NO_2]^4[O_2]}{[N_2O_5]^2}$

3. $K_c = \dfrac{[CH_3OH]}{[CO][H_2]^2}$

4. $K_c = \dfrac{[N_2]^2[H_2O]^6}{[NH_3]^4[O_2]^3}$

5. $K_c = \dfrac{[NO_2]^4}{[N_2O]^2[O_2]^3}$

Summary Questions Chapter 7

1. a) $K_c = \dfrac{[NO_2]^2}{[N_2O_4]}$

   b) $K_c = \dfrac{[SiCl_4][H_2]^2}{[SiH_4][Cl_2]^2}$

   c) $K_c = \dfrac{[PCl_3]^2[Br_2]^3}{[PBr_4]^2[Cl_2]^3}$

   d) $K_c = \dfrac{[CH_3OH]}{[CO][H_2]^2}$

   e) $K_c = \dfrac{[NO]^2[O_2]}{[NO_2]^2}$

2. a) Colour darkens as equilibrium shifts right to reduce the number of moles of gas.

   b) The reverse reaction is endothermic, therefore the colour lightens.

   c) A catalyst has no effect as it lowers the activation energy of the forward and reverse reactions equally.

   d) Addition of a noble gas has no effect.

   e) The equilibrium will shift right to use up the excess oxygen added.

Learning Check 8.1

a) $HNO_3(aq) + NaHCO_3(aq) \rightarrow NaNO_3(aq) + H_2O(l) + CO_2(g)$

b) $Al_2O_3(s) + 6HCl(aq) \rightarrow 2AlCl_3(aq) + 3H_2O(l)$

c) $ZnO(s) + H_2SO_4(aq) \rightarrow ZnSO_4(aq) + H_2O(l)$

d) $Mg(s) + 2HNO_3(aq) \rightarrow Mg(NO_3)_2(aq) + H_2(g)$

e) $H_2SO_4(aq) + CuCO_3(s) \rightarrow CuSO_4(aq) + H_2O(l) + CO_2(g)$

f) $2HCl(aq) + Ca(OH)_2(aq) \rightarrow CaCl_2(aq) + 2H_2O(l)$

Learning Check 8.2

1. a) HF b) $N_2H_5^+$

   c) $C_5H_6N^+$ d) HO_2^-

   e) H_2CrO_4 f) H_2O_2

2. a) NH_2^- b) CO_3^{2-}

   c) CN^- d) $H_4IO_6^-$

   e) NO_3^- f) OH^-

3. a) acid, base $\rightleftharpoons$ conjugate base, conjugate acid

   b) base, acid $\rightleftharpoons$ conjugate acid, conjugate base

   c) acid, base $\rightleftharpoons$ conjugate base, conjugate acid

   d) acid, base $\rightleftharpoons$ conjugate base, conjugate acid

Chapter 8 Summary

1. a) $2HNO_3(aq) + CuO(s) \rightarrow Cu(NO_3)_2(aq) + H_2O(l)$

   b) $2Al(s) + 6HCl(aq) \rightarrow 2AlCl_3(aq) + 3H_2(g)$

   c) $Fe_2(CO_3)_3(s) + 3H_2SO_4(aq) \rightarrow Fe_2(SO_4)_3(aq) + 3H_2O(l) + 3CO_2(g)$

2. a) HSO_4^- b) HCO_3^-

   c) $C_2H_4O_2^-$ d) NH_3

   e) NH_4^+ f) $H_2PO_4^-$

3. a) I^- b) H^-

   c) NH_3 d) NO_2^-

   e) HPO_4^{2-} f) $H_2PO_4^-$

4. a) acid, base $\rightleftharpoons$ conj. acid, conj. base

   b) base, acid $\rightleftharpoons$ conj. acid, conj. base

   c) base, acid $\rightleftharpoons$ conj. acid, conj. base

   d) acid, base $\rightleftharpoons$ conj. base, conj. acid

Learning Check 9.1

+4	+3	+3	+3
MoS_2	Ni_2O_3	P_4O_6	As_2O_3

+3	+3	+2	+6
$Cr(NO_3)_3$	$Cr_2(SO_4)_3$	$CrSO_4$	$Cr(SO_4)_3$

+1	+3	+5	+7
ClO^-	ClO_2^-	ClO_3^-	ClO_4^-

Learning Check 9.2

1. Yes

2. Yes

3. Yes

4. No

5. No

Learning Check 9.3

1. H_2 is the reducing agent, Cl_2 is the oxidizing agent

2. MnO_2 is the oxidizing agent, the chloride ion is the reducing agent

3. CH_4 is the reducing agent, O_2 is the oxidizing agent.

Summary Questions Chapter 9

+2	+4	+1	+2
CO	CO_2	Hg_2Cl_2	HgO

+7	+5	+6	0
$KMnO_4$	$Mg_2P_2O_7$	$XeOF_4$	As_4

+6	+2	+3	0
$Na_2C_2O_4$	$Na_2S_2O_3$	$HAsO_2$	S_8

Learning Check 10.1

a) 2,4-dimethylhexane
b) 3,4-dimethylhexane
c) 2-methylpentane
d) 2,2-dimethylbutane
e) 2,3-dibromopentane
f) 2,2-dibromopentane
g) 1,3-dichlorobutane

Learning Check 10.2

a) Three isomers of C_5H_{12}

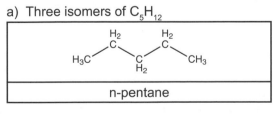

n-pentane

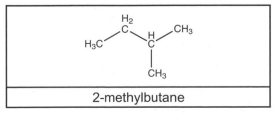

2-methylbutane

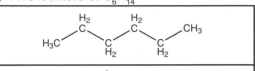

2,2-dimethylpropane

b) Five isomers of C_6H_{14}

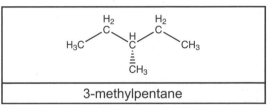

n-hexane

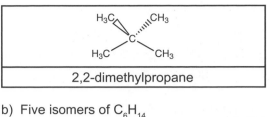

2-methylpentane

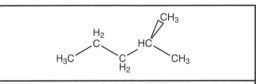

3-methylpentane

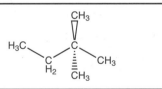

2,2-dimethylbutane

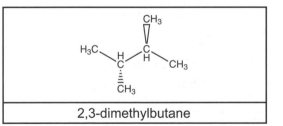

2,3-dimethylbutane

Learning Check 10.3

a) butanoic acid, methyl propanoate, ethyl ethanoate, propyl methanoate

b) pentanal, pentan-2-one, pentan-3-one

Learning Check 10.4

$$CH_4 + 3O_2 \rightarrow CO_2 + 2H_2O$$
$$2C_2H_6 + 7O_2 \rightarrow 4CO_2 + 6H_2O$$
$$C_3H_8 + 5O_2 \rightarrow 3CO_2 + 4H_2O$$
$$2C_4H_{10} + 13O_2 \rightarrow 8CO_2 + 10H_2O$$

Learning Check 10.5

$$2CH_4 + 3O_2 \rightarrow 2CO + 4H_2O$$
$$2C_2H_6 + 5O_2 \rightarrow 4CO + 6H_2O$$
$$2C_3H_8 + 7O_2 \rightarrow 6CO + 8H_2O$$
$$2C_4H_{10} + 9O_2 \rightarrow 8CO + 10H_2O$$

Learning Check 10.6

polybut-2-ene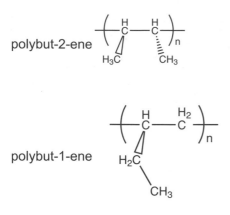

polybut-1-ene

Learning Check 10.7

$$2CH_3OH + 3O_2 \rightarrow 2CO_2 + 4H_2O$$
$$C_2H_5OH + 3O_2 \rightarrow 2CO_2 + 3H_2O$$
$$2C_3H_7OH + 9O_2 \rightarrow 6CO_2 + 8H_2O$$
$$C_4H_9OH + 6O_2 \rightarrow 4CO_2 + 5H_2O$$

Learning Check 10.8

1-chlorohexane
2-chlorohexane
3-chlorohexane
1-chloro-2-methylpentane
2-chloro-2-methylpentane
3-chloro-2-methylpentane
4-chloro-2-methylpentane (2-chloro-4-methylpentane)
5-chloro-2-methylpentane (1-chloro-4-methypentane)
1-chloro-3-methylpentane
2-chloro-3-methylpentane
3-chloro-3-methylpentane
1-chloro-2,2-dimethylbutane
3-chloro-2,2-dimethylbutane
4-chloro-2,2-dimethylbutane (1-chloro-3,3-dimethylbutane)
1-chloro-2,3-dimethylbutane
2-chloro-2,3-dimethylbutane

Learning Check 10.9

a) Heat but-2-ene with steam and a platinum catalyst to form butan-2-ol. Oxidize butan-2-ol with acidified potassium dichromate to from butanone

b) Treat 1-bromobutane with NaOH to form butan-1-ol. Distill butanal from the reaction of butan-1-ol and acidified potassium dichromate.

Learning Check 10.10

1. React ethene with HBr to form bromoethane. Treat bromoethane with hydrogen cyanide to form propanenitrile

2. React 1-bromopropane with aqueous hydroxide to from 1-propanol. Oxidize with acidified potassium dichromate and distill the product.

Chapter 10 Summary Questions

1. a) 2-methylbutane

   b) pentane

   c) 2-methylbutane

   d) 3,4-dimethylhexane

2.

a) butan-1-ol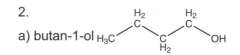

butan-2-ol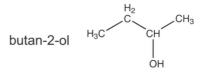

2-methylbutan-1-ol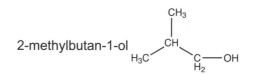

2-methylbutan-2-ol

b) i) butanal, $CH_3CH_2CH_2CHO$

   ii) heat with acidified potassium dichromate during distillation.

c) 2-methylpropan-2-ol

d) Heat the primary alcohols with acidified potassium dichromate under reflux.

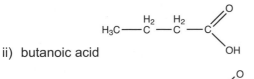

ii) butanoic acid

2-methylpropanoic acid

e) i) The reaction occuring when a species with a lone pair of electrons displaces a leaving group from a carbon bearing a partially positive charge.

ii) $C_4H_9Br + OH^- \rightarrow C_4H_9OH + Br^-$

iii) 2-methylpropan-2-ol formed from 2-bromo-2-methylpropane

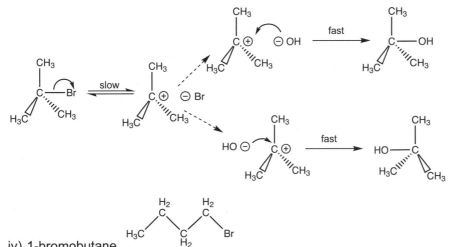

iv) 1-bromobutane

Learning Check 11.1

a) 3 s.d.   b) 3

c) 3   d) 4

e) 4   f) 3

Learning Check 11.2

a) 2200   b) 0.035

c) 2.00   d) 0.026

e) 0.00501   f) 2150

Learning Check 11.3

a) 5.87   b) 14.98

c) 0.0275   d) 0.04

e) 842.4   f) 2.7

g) 2.7   h) 12000